Quilting
Through the Year

a collection of primary quilts

by Paula Symonds

A Teaching Resource Center Publication

Acknowledgments

I give many thanks to: Principal Leslie Lohmeier of Sunnybrae School in San Mateo, CA for putting up with me; Sunnybrae School kindergarten teachers Lynn Azzopardi, Judy Brumm, and Emma Scott, and first grade teachers Maile Sweeney, Pam Heyda, and Linda Doherty for their feedback, ideas, patience, hours of time, and especially their friendship and camaraderie; and first, second, or third grade teacher (depending on the year!) June Tanamachi, for bringing me to Sunnybrae in the first place.

I give my admiration and thanks to the children of Sunnybrae School for teaching me how to organize the lessons and ask the right questions, and for showing me just how remarkable young learners can be.

I give special thanks to Maile Sweeney for designing the Flower and Raindrop quilt and Judy Brumm for designing the Rainbow Fish quilt.

Finally, I could not have completed this book without:
the quiet insistence of Ken Poe,
the patient and creative guidance of Anne Linehan,
the artistic mastery of Janis Poe,
the editing of Laura Woodard.

Thank you all!

Published by
Teaching Resource Center
P.O. Box 82777
San Diego, CA 92138

Edited by Anne Linehan & Laura Woodard
Design and production by Janis Poe & Lisa Chase

Printed in the United States of America
ISBN: 1-56785-044-8

Contents

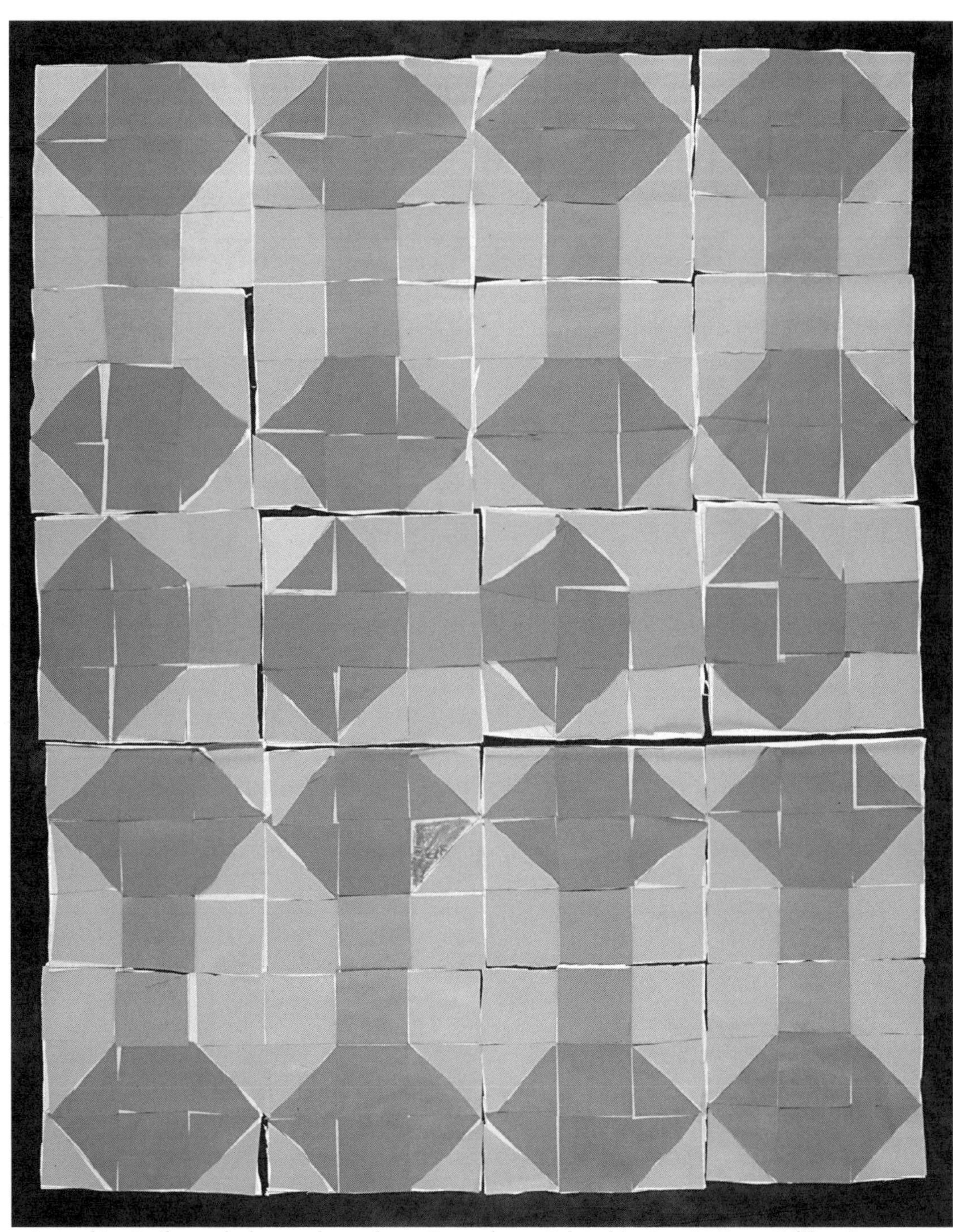

Pumpkin Quilt made by students from Sunnybrae School in San Mateo, California.
See a color version of this quilt on the back cover.

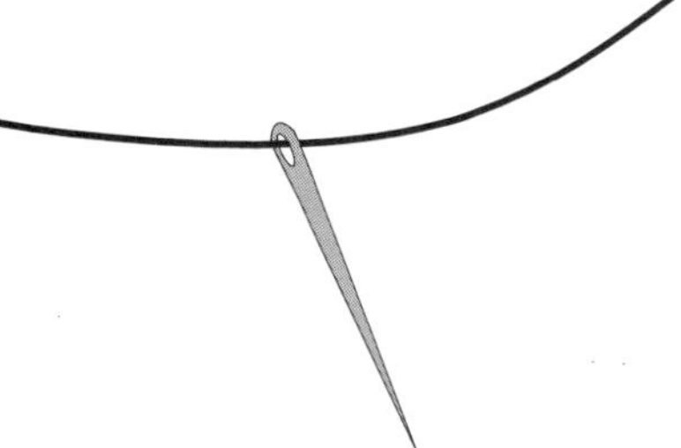

Introduction

Why this book?

Classroom quilting has become very popular. Children's book authors have contributed wonderful stories to enrich this quilting experience, while many teachers have recognized the fact that quilting is a great vehicle for teaching mathematics, especially geometry.

As teachers experienced my quilting ideas at conferences and summer workshops, they asked me for more. Soon I found myself spending a great deal of time filling envelopes with quilting lessons and sending them off in the mail. As the quilting folder on my computer filled, I realized that I had enough ideas for a book. With the encouragement of Ken Poe of Teaching Resource Center, I set to work.

Quilting Through the Year is meant to serve a variety of needs. It is filled with art activities, two for each month, which use quilting to teach and reinforce a variety of math skills. This book models ways to ask questions that encourage children to experiment with their ideas as they develop problem solving skills. In the end it brings children together to make something beautiful that they could not have easily made alone.

Who is this book for?

This book is for teachers of kindergarten through second grade. The lessons are designed to meet the developmental needs of children at this level. Second grade students with no classroom experience in paper quilting will be challenged by many of the quilts. They will approach the lessons with more self-assurance and independence. They need less guidance in the assembly process, and more challenging mathematics.

Second grade teachers can extend these lessons in the area of math using *Math By All Means: Geometry, Grades 1-2* by Chris Confer as a guide.

How is this book organized?

This book is divided into three parts: Introduction, The Mathematics of the Quilt, and the quilt lessons which are organized by month and include blackline masters. For each month of the year there are two quilt lessons: one is more appropriate for kindergarten students (level 1), and the other for first and second graders (level 2). The level 1 quilts are also appropriate for those first graders who have had no quilting experience.

How are the lessons organized?

The lessons are organized to address the needs of a diverse group of teachers:

• those who teach integrated lessons
Ideas are provided at the beginning of each lesson for connecting that lesson with literature, science, history, and/or the season.

• those who want to enrich their math teaching
Each lesson highlights the math skills taught and refers the teacher to the appropriate section in The Mathematics of the Quilt for a description of how to teach the concept. These references are provided in sidebars throughout the lesson.

example:

See Hidden Patterns and Designs, page 22, for a complete discussion of exploring patterns in finished quilts.

• the experienced teacher
Each lesson contains a synopsis and a materials list. The teacher can read the synopsis for a quick overview of the lesson, see what materials need to be prepared, and get right to work.

• those who wish to teach quilting as an art activity
Each lesson contains step-by-step directions for putting the quilt together along with illustrated examples of the finished quilt and the needed blackline masters.

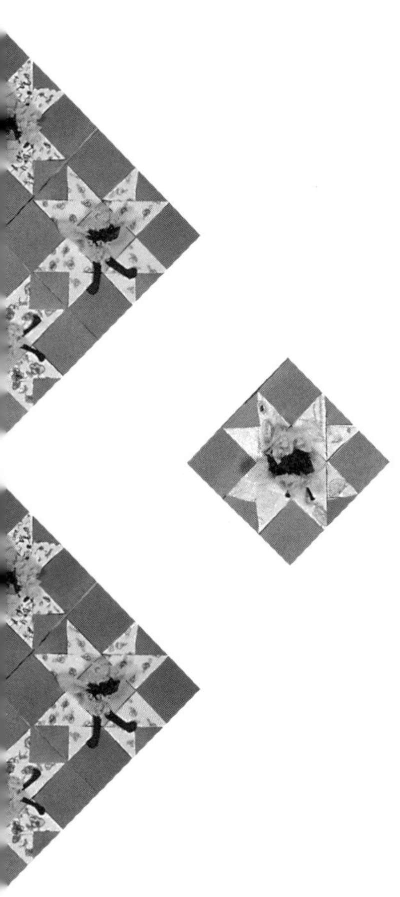

Lesson Synopsis

The Synopsis provides the expert teacher with a snapshot of the lesson and the less experienced teacher with a lesson outline.

Materials

All the materials are listed at the beginning of the lesson so the teacher can collect and cut everything needed for the lesson at one time. Always cut a few extra paper squares to have on hand for mistakes and experimentation.

A note about the materials:
The size of the quilt pieces varies from quilt to quilt. Make sure you read the cutting directions for each quilt carefully. There is nothing worse than cutting pieces for a class of 20-30 only to discover that they are too small or too large to fit on the blackline master.

Introducing the Quilt

This section provides a literature introduction for each quilt and ideas for integrating the quilt lesson into a science, history, or seasonal unit. A complete bibliography is on page 164 for additional book ideas. Incorporate your favorite books on the theme if the suggested titles are not available.

Making the Quilt Block

Some lessons involve making one kind of quilt block, while others involve making two. This part of the lesson is where some of the most active (and often most challenging) mathematical explorations take place. I've tried to give the teacher a feel for what it is like to discuss and construct quilt blocks with a class. I especially wanted teachers to focus on the sample questions. It is important that teachers' questions facilitate problem solving. It is equally important that the children be allowed to talk through their ideas and solutions and verify the results on their own. Children, as we all know, learn more from their own discoveries than from answers that are given to them.

Assembling the Quilt

There are many ways a quilt might be assembled. The lessons explore a variety of assemblage techniques and each focuses on different mathematical explorations.

- using arrays to find a good size for the quilt,
- assembling the quilt in a particular pattern,
- exploring many patterns and choosing one everyone likes,
- experimenting with the quilt pieces to find the best arrangement,
- working together in groups of four to find a four-block pattern that will be repeated to form the finished quilt,
- discovering that some quilts have only one way to be assembled, and
- putting quilt blocks together to create pictures (snowmen emerge from snowballs, chicks emerge from squares and rectangle).

All the quilt blocks are finally glued onto bulletin board paper or any other paper that comes in large sections. A paper color is suggested for each quilt because the paper's edges serve as the border of the quilt. Sometimes it is necessary to tape sections of bulletin board paper together in order to get the size that is best for the quilt being assembled.

What is the best arrangement for the quilt blocks?

Teachers may need to take some time to experiment on their own with the quilt construction. The quilts are seldom arranged or assembled on the same day the quilt blocks are completed, as the blocks need to be set aside to dry. Once the children have gone home, the teacher can play with the blocks to become comfortable with the range of assembly possibilities for the quilt before the children are faced with the assembly process. This knowledge is useful for guiding the students in their explorations and allows flexibility in design for each time a teacher repeats a quilt lesson.

Searching for Patterns and Designs

This is the part of the lesson where the children have the opportunity to admire their finished quilt and look for any new patterns or designs that may have emerged because of the way they chose to put the quilt together. What the children say can be recorded on paper idea bubbles and displayed on the wall with the quilt.

Do the lessons progress in difficulty?

The lessons are arranged in order of difficulty in both the construction of the quilt blocks and the mathematics presented. Knowing a teacher might buy this book in February and want to jump right in, I included details in each lesson that might have been introduced earlier. This makes some parts of the lessons a little repetitive, but it eliminates the need to constantly refer the reader to earlier sections. First grade teachers also have the option of choosing the level 1 quilt as their starting point, for it will always be somewhat simpler than the level 2 quilt.

Depending on the starting point, kindergarten teachers will have more difficulty making the quilts out of sequence if their students have had no previous experience with paper quilting. Those quilts that have two different sizes of triangles or have many small triangles to cut and place will be very tough for first-time quilters. The time spent making the quilt blocks should be extended so the children have ample time to experiment with cutting and placing pieces. Remember not to put out glue until the children feel confident they have cut and placed the pieces correctly. A sidebar in every lesson reminds you of this because it is always easier to move or change pieces that aren't sticky.

DON'T put glue on the tables until everyone has placed his or her pieces correctly.

Should children make each quilt only once?

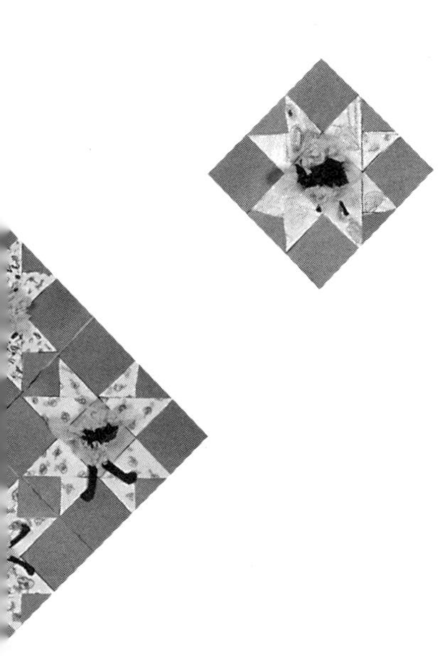

The making of each quilt is a unique experience. A quilt made in kindergarten is different when made in first grade. The older children bring new ideas and more advanced skills to the lesson. A novice first grade teacher might want to start with the simpler level 1 quilt to feel comfortable with the quilting process. If teachers love a quilt and want to make it regardless of whether the children have made it previously, they can vary the materials, introduce more complex mathematics, or challenge the children to invent new arrangements. Experimentation, flexibility, and creativity are important skills to practice, not only for children, but also for teachers.

Let quilting remain a personal experience. If you love a quilt, do it. Don't worry that it may have been done before. Many fabric quilters repeat designs, varying the fabric or arrangement, and each time the new quilt is beautiful and unique.

These quilts are meant as starting points. Explore the joy of creating something beautiful and have fun!

The Mathematics of the Quilt

Shape Recognition

The first challenge children must meet in paper quilting is recognizing the shapes needed to make the quilt block. This is not as big a challenge in first grade as it is in kindergarten. Quilting does provide a relevant context in which to teach shapes.

It is important to study the quilt you plan to make and decide what difficulties shape recognition might pose to your class. When you begin a new quilt, have ready large construction paper pieces in the shapes required for the lesson.

square

1. 4 sides \\\\\\\\
2. 4 corners ┌ ┐ └ ┘
3. all 4 sides are the same | | | |
4. the corners make *L*'s └

Begin with a square, since all the shapes used in the quilts are generated from squares. Have the children describe what they see. List the attributes on the square as they point them out.

Once they have finished, show the children one of the small squares that will be used for the quilt. Ask them how it is similar to the large square. Ask if they think they can name the smaller shape.

Teacher: *Both these shapes have four sides, and both have four corners. Both have all four sides the same, and the corners make L's. What do you think the name of this shape is?* (She holds up the smaller square.)
Richard: *Is it a square?*
Teacher: *You don't seem sure.*
Richard: *It's smaller.*
Teacher: *Do you think the different size might give it a different name?*
Roxanne: *Squares are squares. It doesn't matter the size.*
Teacher: *Are you sure?*
Children: *Yes. It doesn't matter. It's just a big square.*

Post the large paper square so you can refer to it whenever necessary. Repeat this activity for whatever shapes are used in making the quilt block.

Spatial Problem Solving

As adults, it is quite easy for us to identify and place a shape correctly, especially with the given quilts. For many kindergartners and some first graders, this is not so easy. It is important to model placement of the shapes so you can give the children both visual and auditory guidelines to help them as they work on their own.

Teacher: *Who thinks they can come and put this square where it goes?* (Many hands go up.) *Heather.*
Watch how Heather very carefully lines up the square so it fits just inside the lines. It's nice and straight. It's not crooked. Quilters are always very careful to put the shapes right where they go.

Placing a triangle provides a special challenge for many kindergartners and some first graders.

Teacher: *It is sometimes very hard to get the triangle to fit right. Sometimes you just have to keep turning it until it fits in place.* (Tiffany is struggling, turning and turning the shape.) *When you turn the triangle, you have to go very slowly so you don't miss where it fits.* (Hubson just can't seem to get the triangle in place.) *Sometimes it helps to find the longest side of the triangle and match it with the longest side in the picture.* (Hubson matches longest to longest, and finally the triangle fits!)

Never put the shapes in place for the child. Use a variety of cues and a good dose of patience. Some children have highly developed spatial sense, while others have great difficulty. When I taught kindergarten, I got a tremendous amount of exercise helping a girl named Claudia, using as much body language as I could muster, to get those shapes where they needed to go. She was as exhausted as I was each time she had finished a quilt block. In first grade it wasn't quite so hard, but those triangles still gave her a tough time. In second grade she had it! She was good at it, and her skill will serve her in good stead when she later takes geometry in junior high and high school.

Congruence

Shapes are *congruent* if they have the same size and form. Young children can learn this term easily when it is given in a clear context of matching a paper shape to shape in the quilt block. This sometimes requires flipping a paper triangle so it faces the same way as a triangle on the quilt block before comparing the two shapes (see illustration). Model for the children the act of matching so they don't just assume shapes are congruent. This tool of proof is important.

Triangles and Halves

Many quilts in this book are composed of triangles and squares. Each time the children are faced with constructing a quilt, they are given only squares with which to cover the quilt block. Their challenge is to find a way to make triangles from squares. The first time you present this problem, give them extra paper squares and scissors with which to experiment.

The problem of making triangles is less a challenge for first graders than it is for kindergartners. Many kindergartners begin by cutting the square until its shape approximates that of a triangle. They pay little

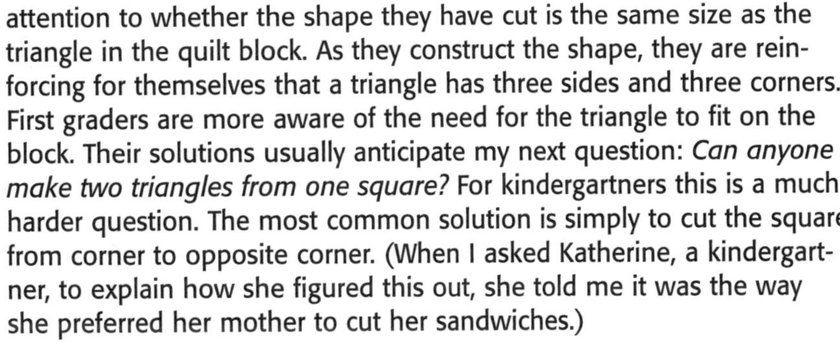

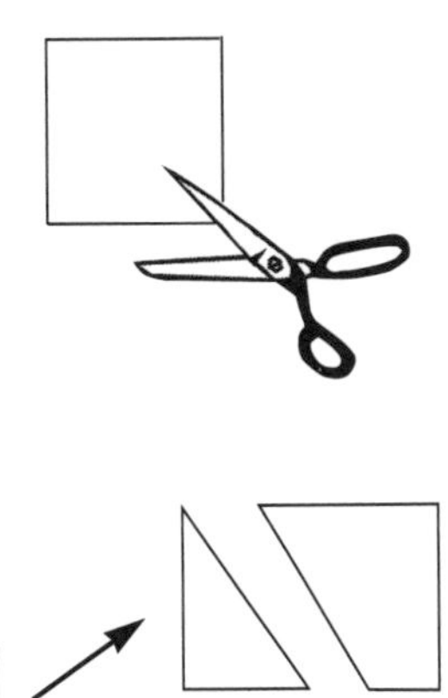

attention to whether the shape they have cut is the same size as the triangle in the quilt block. As they construct the shape, they are reinforcing for themselves that a triangle has three sides and three corners. First graders are more aware of the need for the triangle to fit on the block. Their solutions usually anticipate my next question: *Can anyone make two triangles from one square?* For kindergartners this is a much harder question. The most common solution is simply to cut the square from corner to opposite corner. (When I asked Katherine, a kindergartner, to explain how she figured this out, she told me it was the way she preferred her mother to cut her sandwiches.)

As the children experiment, some are not as precise as others. Some get triangles and an odd, four-sided shape. Others get triangles with one very crooked side.

At this point I show them a large triangle and ask if one of the sides is wiggly. They agree that all three sides are straight. I ask if there is a way to make sure their cutting is very straight. Some suggest that they cut very slowly, heading carefully for the opposite corner. Some suggest folding the square to make a triangle and show that after it is unfolded they get two triangles with all the sides straight. Then they just cut on the fold line to produce the two separate triangles.

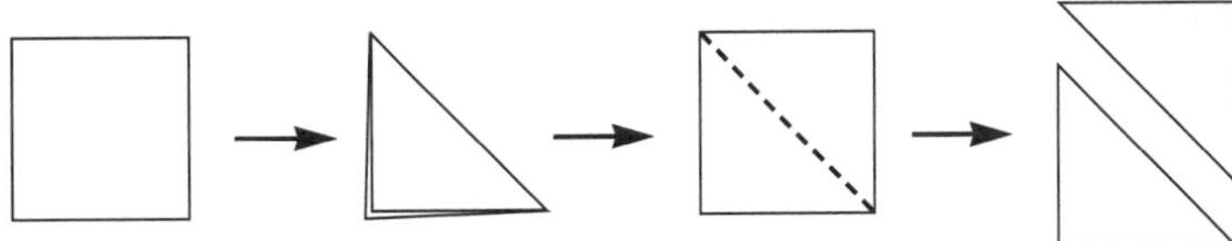

This is not a popular choice for kindergartners, as folding requires considerable manual dexterity. More first graders prefer this method.

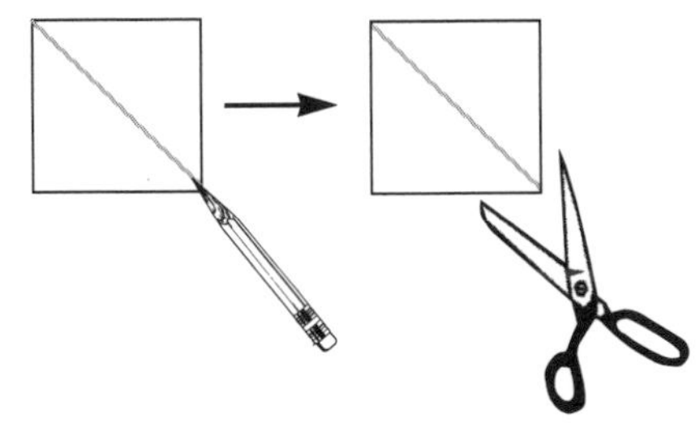

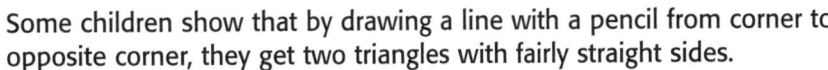

Some children show that by drawing a line with a pencil from corner to opposite corner, they get two triangles with fairly straight sides.

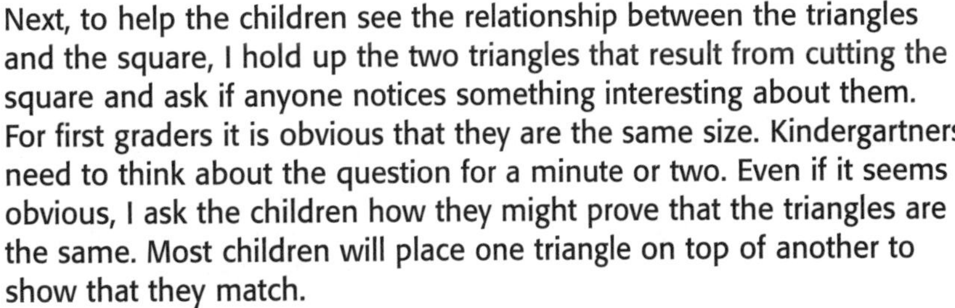

Next, to help the children see the relationship between the triangles and the square, I hold up the two triangles that result from cutting the square and ask if anyone notices something interesting about them. For first graders it is obvious that they are the same size. Kindergartners need to think about the question for a minute or two. Even if it seems obvious, I ask the children how they might prove that the triangles are the same. Most children will place one triangle on top of another to show that they match.

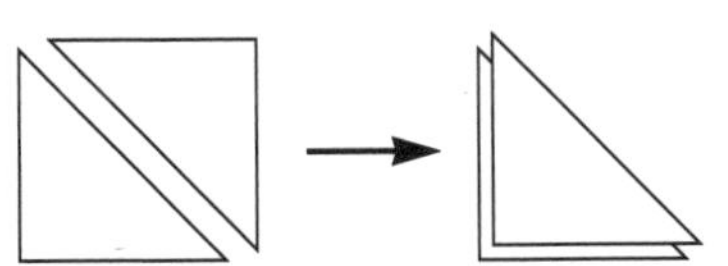

I point out that since the two triangles used up the whole square and they are the same size, they are called halves of the square. I state the rule: *If you divide something into two parts, and the two parts are the same size, each part is one-half of the original piece.*

Despite all the preparation, some children do not apply what they have just practiced to the quilt block. They chop up their squares to make triangles or simply cut up confetti to fill the triangle space on the quilt block. For these children it will take several quilting experiences before they truly understand. Therefore each time you begin a new quilt, you will have to ask how to get two triangles out of a square, and have volunteers show how it is done.

Rectangles and Halves

Some of the quilts in this book contain rectangles. Since the children are always given only squares to start, they must find a way to get rectangles from squares. The first time you give the children this problem, give them extra paper squares and scissors with which to experiment.

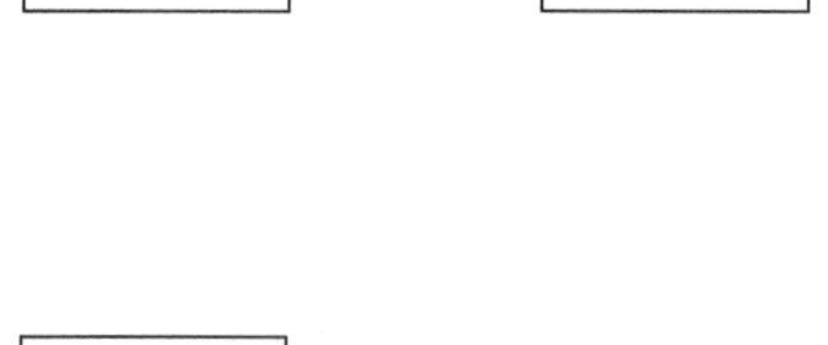

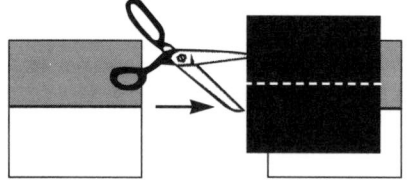

Challenge the children to find a way to get a rectangle that will fit on the quilt block. Most kindergartners simply begin to cut. First graders are more discriminating. They place the square next to the rectangle on the block and examine how it doesn't fit. Some say, "It's the same this way but longer this way."

First graders tend to eyeball a mark and cut. Once they have cut and the rectangle fits, I can ask them what they notice about the remaining rectangle. As they see both are the same size, they realize that folding the square would also be a good solution. They have learned from their folding experiences in kindergarten.

For kindergartners, the idea of folding the square in half to get two congruent rectangles is not so obvious. As they cut and realize their rectangles are either too big or too small, they begin to refine their thinking or look around for help. I encourage the children to look at what others are doing, and I remind them that the rectangle must fit on the quilt block. Some kindergartners will match, compare and cut much like first graders. Most of the time the folding solution is not evident. I must admit that I have often demonstrated the folding only after they have arrived at solutions of their own. Still, folding is hard, and early in the year only a few will choose to do it.

Once the children realize that the two rectangles they got from cutting the square are congruent, I point out that they are also called halves of the square, and I give the rule: *If you divide something into two parts, and the two parts are the same size, each part is one-half of the original piece.*

Triangles and Quarters

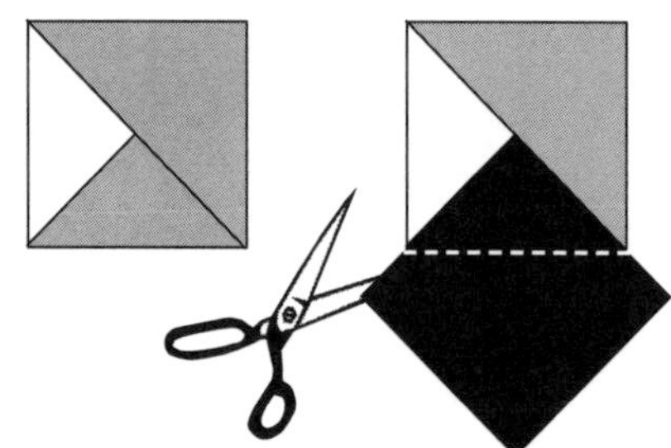

Several of the quilts contain triangles that equal one quarter of the square. The first time kindergartners and first graders encounter these small triangles, they are surprised and unsure of how to proceed. Make sure all the children have access to scissors and paper squares with which to experiment.

The most popular solution is to place the paper square over the small triangle and trim the square until it is the right shape and size.

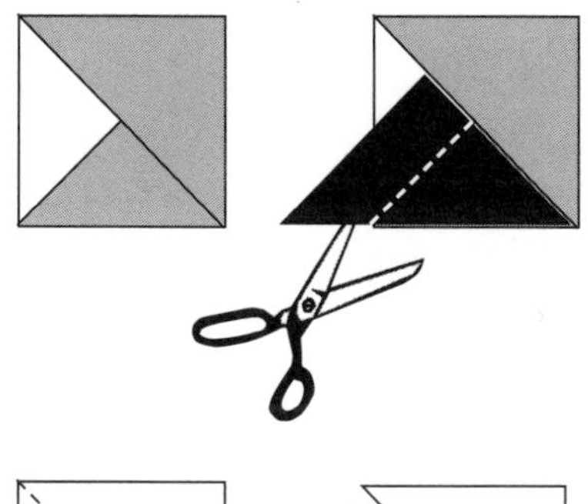

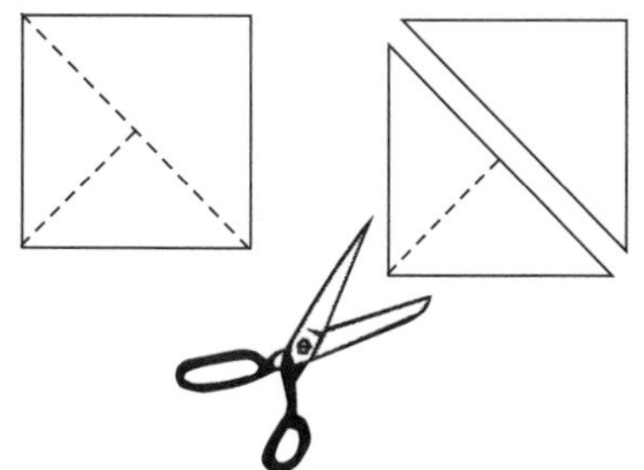

I point out that this is an excellent solution, but there are other ways. First, I give them a hint: they should cut the square to get two triangles. Once they go back to work, I encourage them to share their ideas. Some children now put the large triangle over the smaller triangle and trim it to fit.

But others, especially first graders, notice that the small triangle is half of the larger one. Some, usually only first graders, fold and cut the large triangle in half. Others eyeball half and cut. You may need to demonstrate these strategies for kindergartners. However, when the children go to work on their own to complete the quilt block, they use whichever method they understand the best. Over time and with experience, cutting the triangle in half will become easier.

Once the children have four small triangles, I challenge them to reassemble the four into the square. For those children who are spatially challenged, this is very hard. I remind everyone it might be easiest to make the two large triangles first and then form them into the square. Once everyone has worked together to reassemble the square, I can begin a discussion of one-quarter.

Teacher: *How many little triangles does it take to make the square?*
Children: *It takes four.*
Teacher: *How many large triangles does it take to make a square?*
Children: *It takes two.*
Teacher: *How much of the square is the large triangle?*
Children: *One-half.*
Teacher: *How much of the square is the little triangle?*
Andrew: *Half of a half.*
Teacher: *What do you mean?*
Andrew: *We cut the square in half. So that's half. Then we cut the triangle in half. That's half of a half.*
Teacher: *Excellent, Andrew. Mathematicians have another name for half of a half. They call it one-quarter.*
Andrew: *Oh. Like a quarter. There are four quarters in a dollar.*
Teacher: *Exactly.*

Only a few of the children will see this at first. With more experience the others will come to understand the concept of one-quarter as well.

Early Experiences in Area

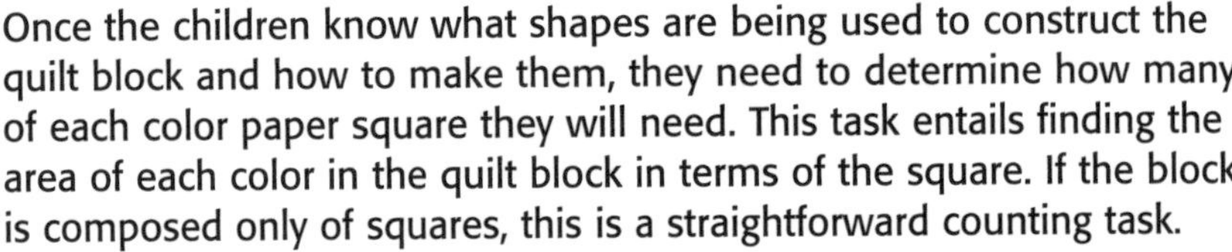

Once the children know what shapes are being used to construct the quilt block and how to make them, they need to determine how many of each color paper square they will need. This task entails finding the area of each color in the quilt block in terms of the square. If the block is composed only of squares, this is a straightforward counting task.

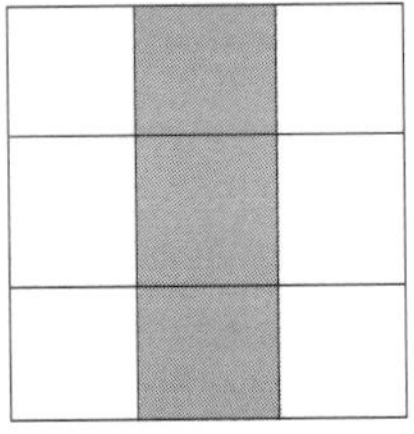

There are three shaded squares and six white squares in the quilt block shown to the left. The area of the shaded part is three and the area of the white part is six. The total area of the block is nine.

If the block contains squares and triangles, or squares and rectangles, the problem is more complex. The children need to keep in mind that two large triangles make a square, and that one large triangle is half of a square, when determining how many squares of each color they will need.

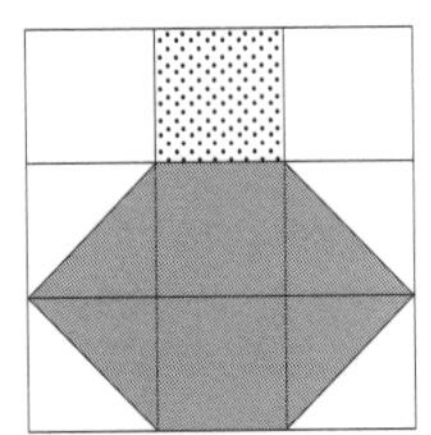

In the quilt block shown here, children can easily see that they will need one dotted square. When they are counting the shaded area, they must remember that two triangles make one square, so it will take four orange squares to cover the shaded area. Most kindergartners will count it as six, not because they don't know that they will get two triangles if they cut a square, but rather they are not yet ready for the two-for-one counting that is required. With kindergartners I start with a number of paper squares and keep track of the amount used as we cover the area. A small lap chalkboard and chalk work well for keeping the tally.

Teacher: *Can someone come up and show me where this orange square goes?* (Kate comes and places the square.) *Put one tally on the chalkboard.* (Kate adds one tally.) *Can someone come and show me where this next orange square goes?* (Salvador comes up and places the square.) *Put one tally on the chalkboard.* (Salvador adds one tally.) *Can we put down any more squares?*
Children: *No. Only triangles.*
Teacher: *How many triangles will we need?*
Children: *Four.*
Teacher: *How many squares is that?*
Children: *Four. No, only two.*
Teacher: *Can someone come up and make triangles to place on the pumpkin?* (Lucy comes and cuts one square to get two triangles. She places the triangles over two shaded triangles.) *How many squares did you use?*
Lucy: *Two. No, one. I used one square.* (She adds one tally to the record.)
Teacher: *How many more squares will we need to finish the pumpkin?*
Children: *Two. No, one.*
Teacher: *Can someone come up and make these triangles?* (Garrett comes and cuts one square, getting two triangles, and places the triangles over the last two shaded triangles. The teacher adds one tally to the record, then covers the tallies.) *How many squares did we use to cover the orange area?* (The children try to recall the number.) *Let's count.*

(She uncovers the record.) *One, two, three, four. We used four orange squares.*

Kindergartners will need a lot of exposure to make sense of this situation. Most first graders who have been exposed to quilting in kindergarten gain mastery easily. If they have had no prior experience, they will need a few lessons as described above.

Finally, if the quilt is composed of squares and large and small triangles, we have a very tricky problem. This problem is over the heads of most kindergartners. However, I think it is important to expose them to it anyway. It is also a very difficult problem for first graders. The children must be able to count by ones, then change to two-for-one counting, and finally change again to four-for-one counting. You're not looking for mastery here but rather exposure.

Vanessa counts triangles as two for one, touching in twos.

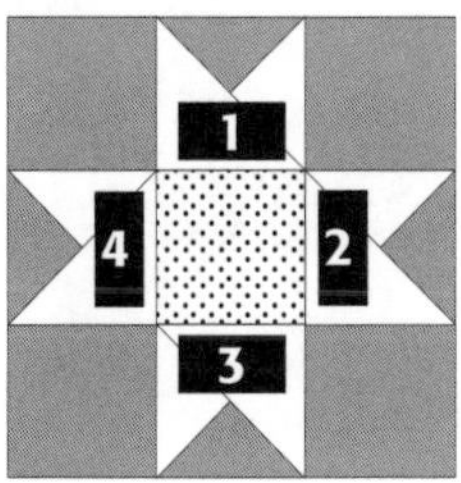

To compute the area of the flower petals and the area of the background in this quilt block, the children must actually cover it. However, always ask questions first to give the children an opportunity to try to figure it out on their own. Have the children share their thinking.

Teacher: *How many squares will we need to cover the flower?*
Children: *Four. Three. Eight.*
Teacher: *Vanessa, why do you think it will take four squares to cover?*
Vanessa: *Because it goes like this:* (touching in twos) *one, two, three, four. It takes four squares.*
Teacher: *Samantha, why do you think it will take eight squares?*
Samantha: *Because it goes like this:* (touching one to one) *one, two, three, four, five, . . . eight. It takes eight.*
Teacher: *Andrew, why do you think it will take three squares?*
Andrew: *Because it goes like this:* (first touching in twos and then in fours) *one, two, three. Three squares.*
Teacher: *Let's see if we can prove who is right.*

Samantha counts triangles as one for one, touching all eight.

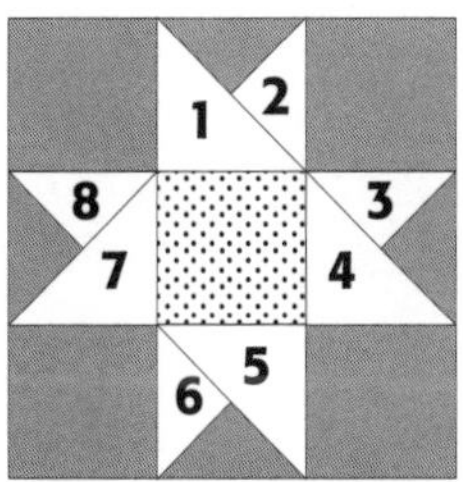

Have the children take turns cutting and placing pieces as one child records the square tally. Count the tally when all the pieces have been placed.

Andrew correctly counts large triangles as halves and small triangles as quarters.

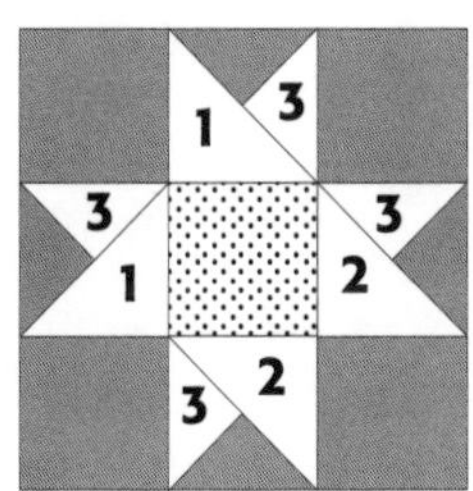

Teacher: *How many squares did it take?*
Children: *Three. It took three.*
Teacher: *Why did it happen this way?*
Vanessa: *I forgot that it takes four little triangles to make a square.*
Teacher: *That's right. We have to remember that, don't we?*

Slides and Rotations

Different types of symmetry in a quilt block generate different design possibilities when the quilt is assembled. Quilt blocks with full rotational symmetry (each time the block is rotated a quarter turn its design remains the same) generate only one quilt design.

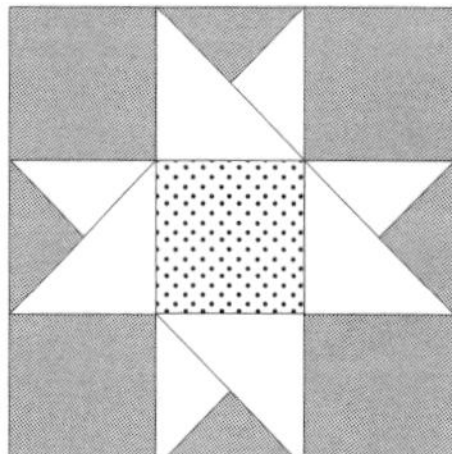

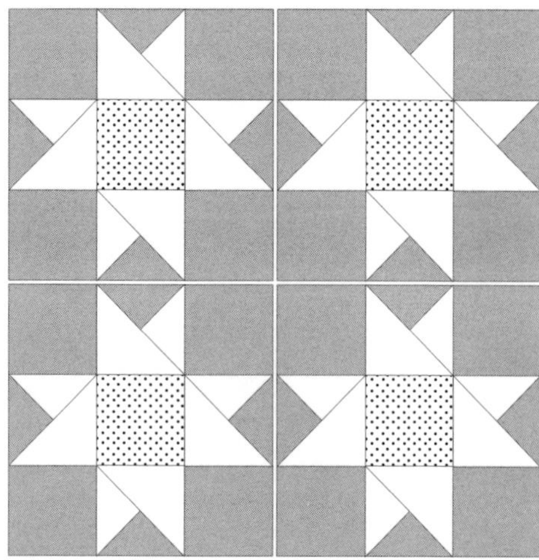

Quilt blocks with one, two, or no lines of symmetry will generate more than one design or pattern depending on how they are arranged in the quilt.

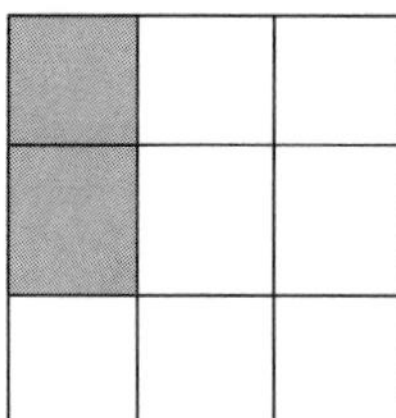

quilt block with no lines of symmetry

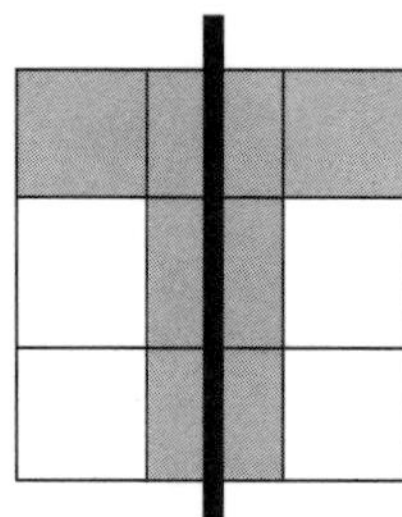

quilt block with only one line of symmetry

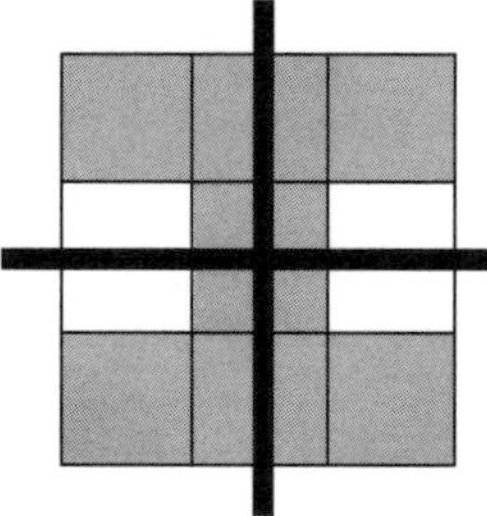

quilt block with two lines of symmetry

Slides

Geometric shapes can be moved in space in different ways. Two ways are by sliding and rotating the shapes. You will show your students how to generate new quilt designs and patterns by using slides and rotations of the quilt blocks. This lesson has the children working in fours so that everyone can have input into the design process.

Gather your students together. Place four quilt blocks in the center of the rug. Explain to the children that you are going to arrange the four blocks into a square.

Take the first block and place it in front of you on the rug. Place the second block on top of the first so its orientation matches. Explain to the children that you are matching the second block to the first. Now slide the second block to the right until it is positioned next to the first. Explain to the children what you are doing:

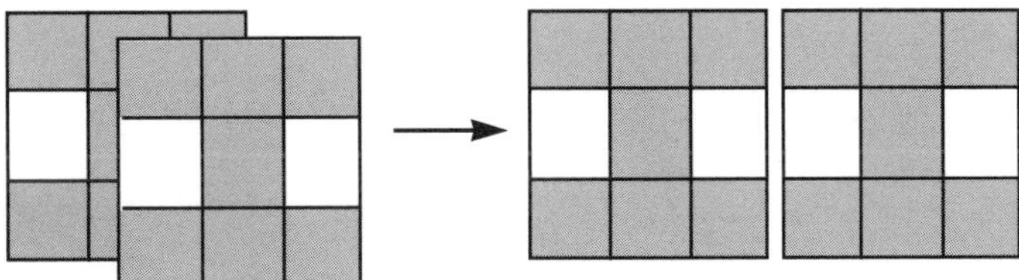

Teacher: *This is called a slide. I'm sliding the block over until it is just next to the first block.*

Match the third block on top of the second. Slide the third block until it is below the second. Explain to the children what you are doing.

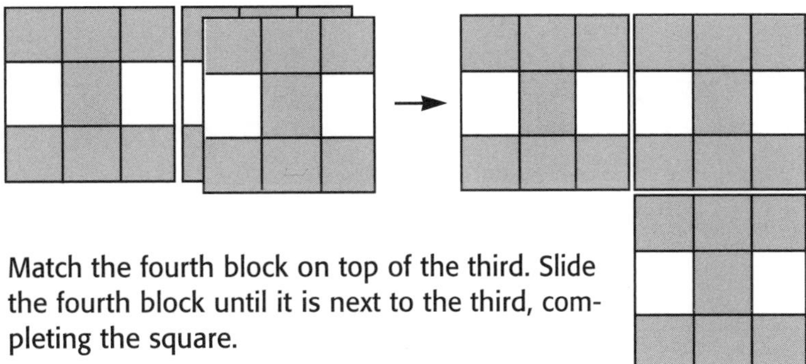

Match the fourth block on top of the third. Slide the fourth block until it is next to the third, completing the square.

Have the children describe the new pattern.

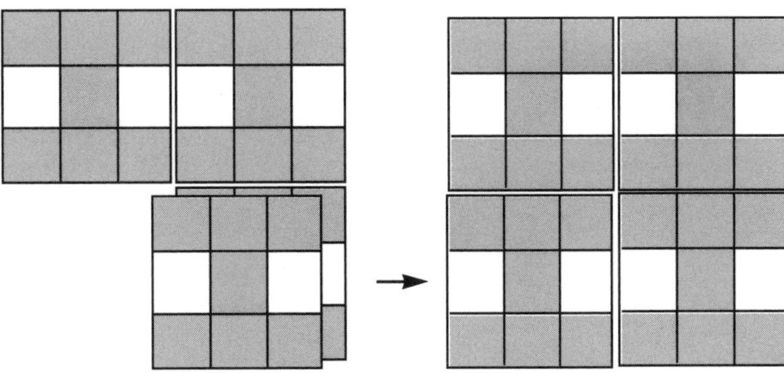

Rotations

Start again with the four separate blocks. Tell the children this time you will move the blocks in a different way to make a new design. Place one block in front of you. Match a second block on top of it. Now rotate the second block one quarter turn and slide it next to the first. Explain to the children what you are doing.

Teacher: *This time I'm matching the block exactly, but before I slide it I'm going to turn it so the top is on the side. I'm going to rotate the block.*

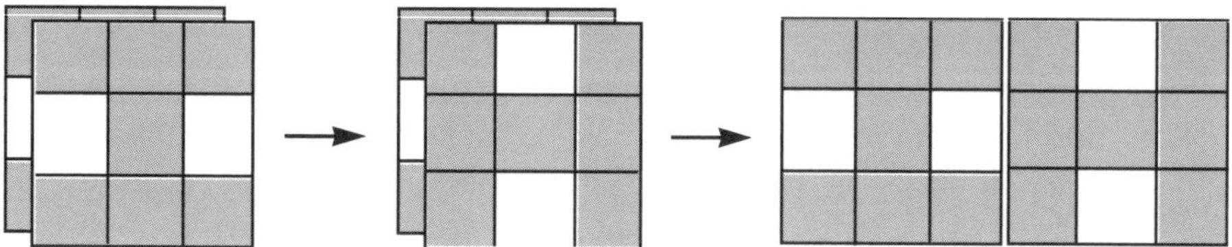

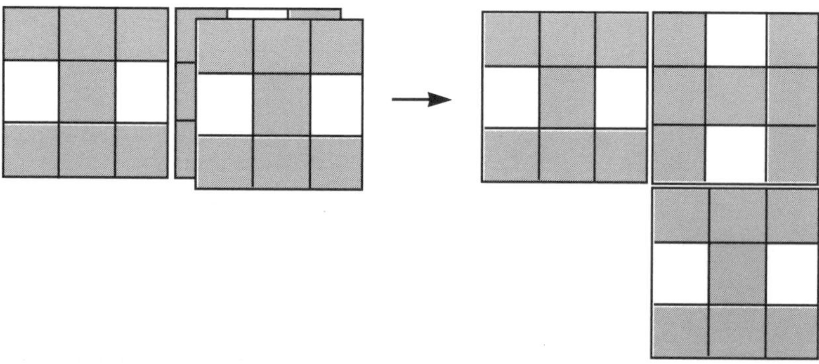

Next, match the third block on top of the second. Rotate the third block one quarter turn and slide it into place below the second. Explain to the children what you are doing.

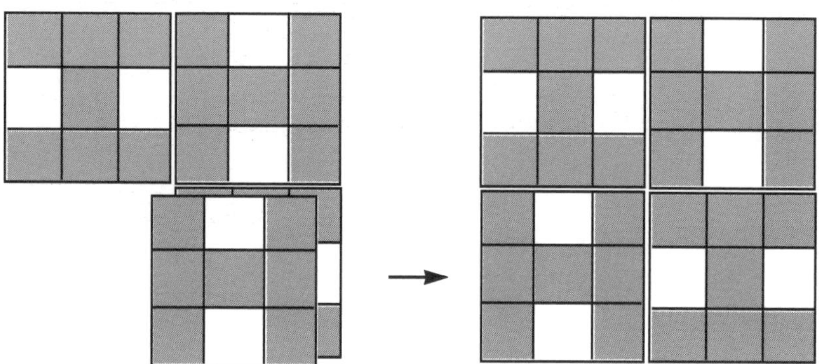

Now, match the fourth block on top of the third block. Turn the fourth block one quarter turn and slide it beside the third block, completing the square.

Have the children describe the new pattern.

Teacher: *What do you notice about the pattern we have made?*
Roxanne: *It's sideways H, straight H.*
Nathaniel: *It's a funny checkerboard.*

After the children have viewed classroom demonstrations, divide them into groups of four. Give each group four quilt blocks. Walk them through the slide and rotation processes explained above, and then tell them that they can experiment sliding and rotating their blocks in different ways to see if they can find any other patterns or designs.

The fewer lines of symmetry in the original block, the more different new designs or patterns will be generated in the quilt.

Computing the Size of the Quilt

Before you discuss the size of the quilt, it is important to decide what shapes are right for a quilt. Discuss with the children whether they have ever seen a triangular quilt. A round quilt? Why? Why not? Most of the children will agree that quilts are usually square or rectangular because these shapes best cover a bed.

Squares and rectangles come in a variety of dimensions. In computing the size of the quilt, discuss what dimensions a good-sized quilt must have. If a quilt were composed of a long line of quilt blocks, it would be too skinny.

Some children describe the quilt above as good for a snake but not for a person.

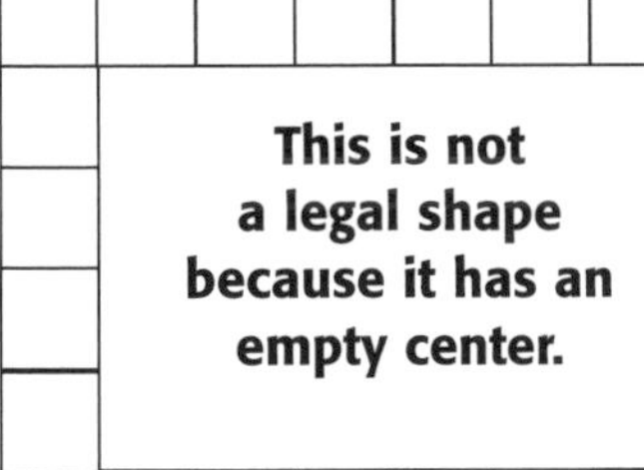

This is not a legal shape because it has an empty center.

Once the children know that the quilt should be a square or a rectangle, but not a long, skinny rectangle, they are ready to begin experimenting on their own. Give partners or small groups a number of 1" ceramic tile equal to the number of quilt blocks the class has made. Challenge the children to arrange the tiles to make a square or a rectangle. The shapes they make cannot have an empty center.

As the children build rectangles or squares, record their shapes on a large sheet of bulletin board paper or on the chalkboard.

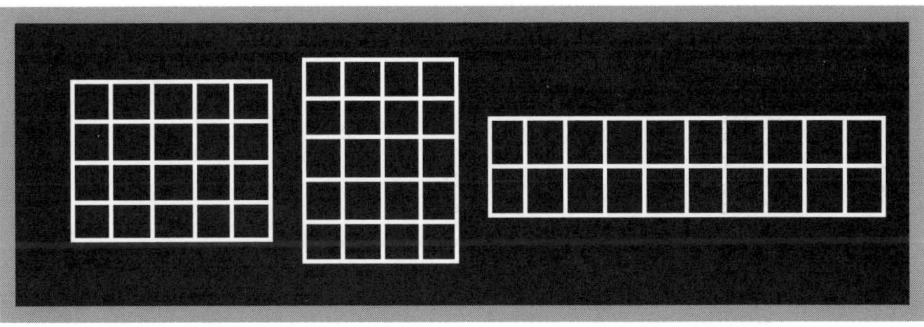

Certain numbers of tiles lend themselves well to making good shapes. For example, twenty-four tiles: twenty-five tiles:

Other numbers of tile, however, can cause problems. For example, twenty-six tiles do not make a good shape for a quilt. (Twenty-six is only divisible by itself, one, thirteen, and two.)

Nineteen doesn't make a good shape either. It only makes a long skinny quilt. (Nineteen is prime, only divisible by itself and one.)

When the children find that the number of blocks does not result in good shapes, challenge them to find new solutions. Some children will suggest taking tiles away. Others will suggest adding tiles. Have the children experiment with both to see which will give them the best quilt shape. Record the shapes they find on chart paper or on the chalkboard for all to see. An example would be twenty-seven tiles:

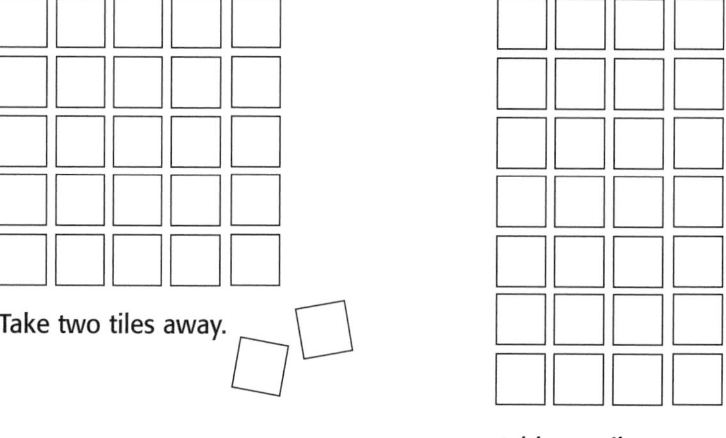
Take two tiles away.
Add one tile.

A more sophisticated solution for this problem which you might suggest is to add or subtract a tile from each corner of the rectangle or square. Quilts made this way cover a bed nicely.

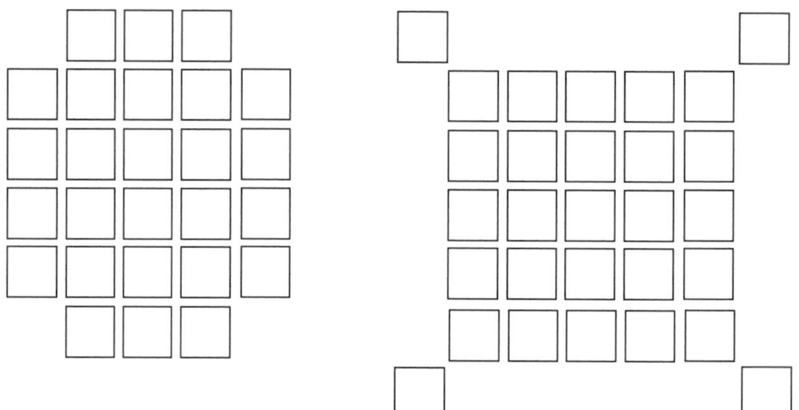

Once the children have found all the shapes they can, have them vote on the shape they prefer for the quilt. If the shape was made by adding blocks, new blocks will need to be made. If the shape was made by taking blocks away, pillows can be made out of the extra blocks.

Occasionally, you will need to assemble a quilt from a linear pattern such as the March pinwheel quilt. Finding a good size for this quilt requires a slightly different process. First the children make a linear pattern with the quilt blocks.

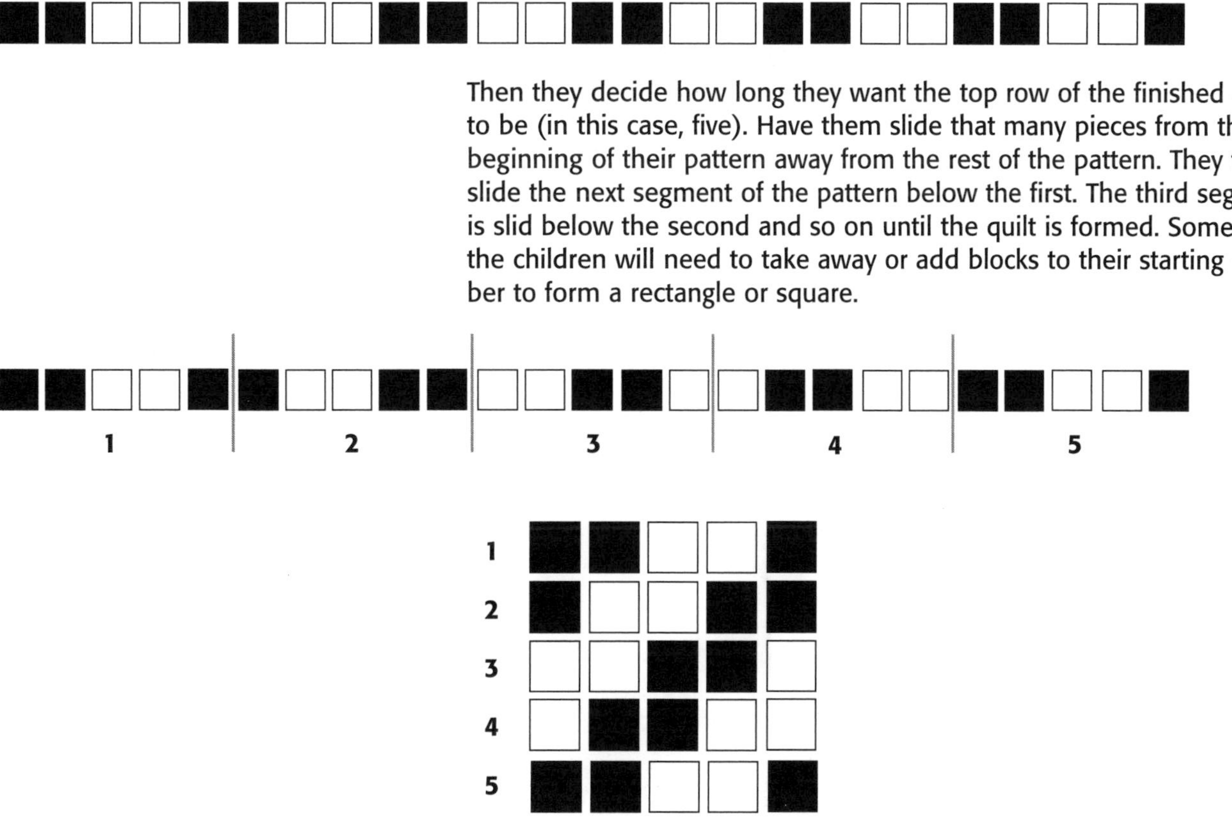

Then they decide how long they want the top row of the finished quilt to be (in this case, five). Have them slide that many pieces from the beginning of their pattern away from the rest of the pattern. They then slide the next segment of the pattern below the first. The third segment is slid below the second and so on until the quilt is formed. Sometimes the children will need to take away or add blocks to their starting number to form a rectangle or square.

This method maintains the starting pattern, but rearranges it as a grid, allowing new patterns to emerge in the finished quilt.

Note: Each time the children build a new shape with the tiles, they are exploring factoring the given number, because the dimensions of the rectangle or square are factors of the total number of blocks. This becomes particularly important when older children do paper quilting, such as when you bring in older buddies to help with a lesson.

Making Quilt Block Pillows

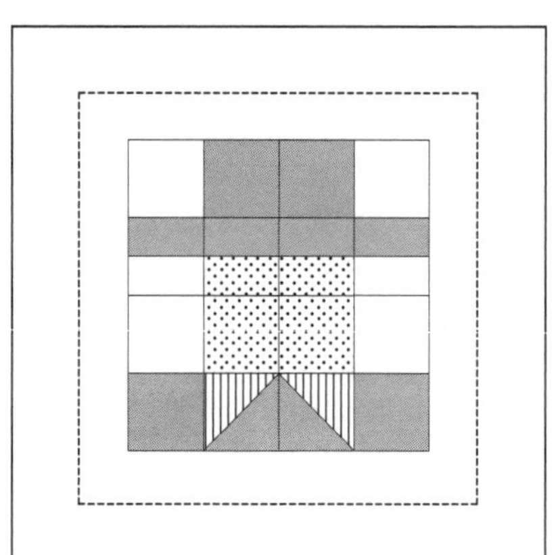

Sometimes you will have leftover quilt blocks. Here's how to make them into pillows.

Materials:
- leftover quilt block(s)
- chart paper
- newspaper
- stapler
- glue

Cut two 2′ x 2′ pieces of chart paper. Glue the leftover quilt block to the center of one piece. Attach the two pieces of paper by stapling around three sides. Place the staples as far in from the edge as possible. Stuff with crumpled newspaper. Staple the last side closed.

Predicting Patterns

Some of the quilts are designed to be assembled in a particular pattern. This allows the children to practice the pattern skills they are learning.

Before each new piece is placed, ask the children to predict what will come next in the pattern. Have them "snap and clap" the pattern to check their choice.

For one of the February quilts, a decorated valentine quilt block and a heart quilt block are placed side by side.

Teacher: *What block comes next?*
Jack: *Valentine.*
Teacher: *How do you know a valentine comes next?*
Jack: *Because it goes valentine, heart, valentine.*
Teacher: *What comes next?*
Roxanne: *A heart.*
Teacher: *Why do you think a heart block comes next?*
Roxanne: *Because next to a valentine always comes a heart.*
Teacher: *Let's "snap and clap" the pattern to check. Snap on valentine, and clap on heart.*
Children: (Snap, clap, snap, clap.)
Teacher: *Are we right?*
Children: *Yes!*

You might challenge the children to predict what block comes later in the pattern.

Teacher: *We need three blocks to fill this row. What will be the last block we place in the row?*
Raymond: *I think it will be a valentine.*
Teacher: *How do you know?*
Raymond: *Because next comes a valentine, then a heart, then a valentine. It will be a valentine.*

Children can be asked to predict the number of each block needed to fill a given row.

Teacher: *How many valentine blocks and heart blocks will we need to fill the next row?*
Katherine: *I think we will need three hearts and four Valentines.*
Teacher: *How did you figure that out?*
Katherine: *I counted on my fingers.* (She says the pattern, keeping track of heart blocks with her right hand and valentine blocks with her left.) *See, three hearts and four Valentines.*

Counting (and Counting in Multiples)

Assembling the quilt provides a perfect opportunity for lots of counting practice. With kindergartners, count the number of blocks in each row as they are placed. Have the children then predict the total blocks placed. Count to check.

Teacher: *Let's count the blocks as we lay them out.*
Children: *One, two, three, four, five, six.*
Teacher: *How many blocks are in the first row?*
Shaina: *Six.*
Teacher: *Let's count as we lay out the next row.*
Children: *One, two, three, four, five, six.*
Teacher: *How many blocks are in the second row?*
Children: *Six.*
Teacher: *If there are six blocks in each row, how many blocks are there altogether?* (There is discussion and counting.)
Richard: *There will be more than ten.*
Teacher: *How do you know?*
Richard: *I counted on my fingers and I ran out.*
Teacher: *How many more fingers do you need?* (Richard counts one, two, three, four, five, six, one, two, three, four, and he nods five, six.)
Richard: *Two more.*
Teacher: *How many will that be?* (Richard looks confused.)
Roxanne: *Twelve. It will be twelve. One, two, three, four, five, six, seven, eight, nine, ten, eleven, twelve.*
Teacher: *How do you know?*
Roxanne: *I counted the blocks.*

With first and second graders, predict the ending number of each row. Count to check. Record the numbers on a chalkboard or chart paper. Read the counting pattern when the children have finished laying out the quilt.

Teacher: *The first row has five blocks. How many blocks do you think there will be altogether when we finish the next row?* (There is discussion and counting.)
Tiffany: *I think there will be ten.*
Teacher: *How did you figure that out?*

Tiffany: *I counted one, two, three, four, five,* (then pointing at empty spaces under the first row) *six, seven, eight, nine, ten. See, ten.*

When the whole quilt is laid out:

Teacher: *Let's read the end of the row numbers we have written.*
Children: *Five, ten, fifteen, twenty, twenty-five, thirty.*
Teacher: *What do you notice about these numbers?*
Heather: *They're "counting by fives" numbers.*

Post the counting pattern next to the quilt so the children will have one more way of visualizing that particular counting pattern.

Hidden Patterns and Designs

The moment the quilt is assembled is magical. The children are always surprised that they have created such a lovely piece of work. As they admire what they have done, they begin to notice new patterns and designs that were not apparent in the single blocks or the squares of four. I encourage the children to talk about what they see. As they talk, I note their observations on paper idea bubbles. Kindergartners love when I write down what they say. They are amazed that they have said something so important as to be noted. Once one pattern is described, others will often describe it repeatedly with subtle differences so their words can fill an idea bubble, too.

Teacher: *What new patterns and designs do you see in our finished quilt?*

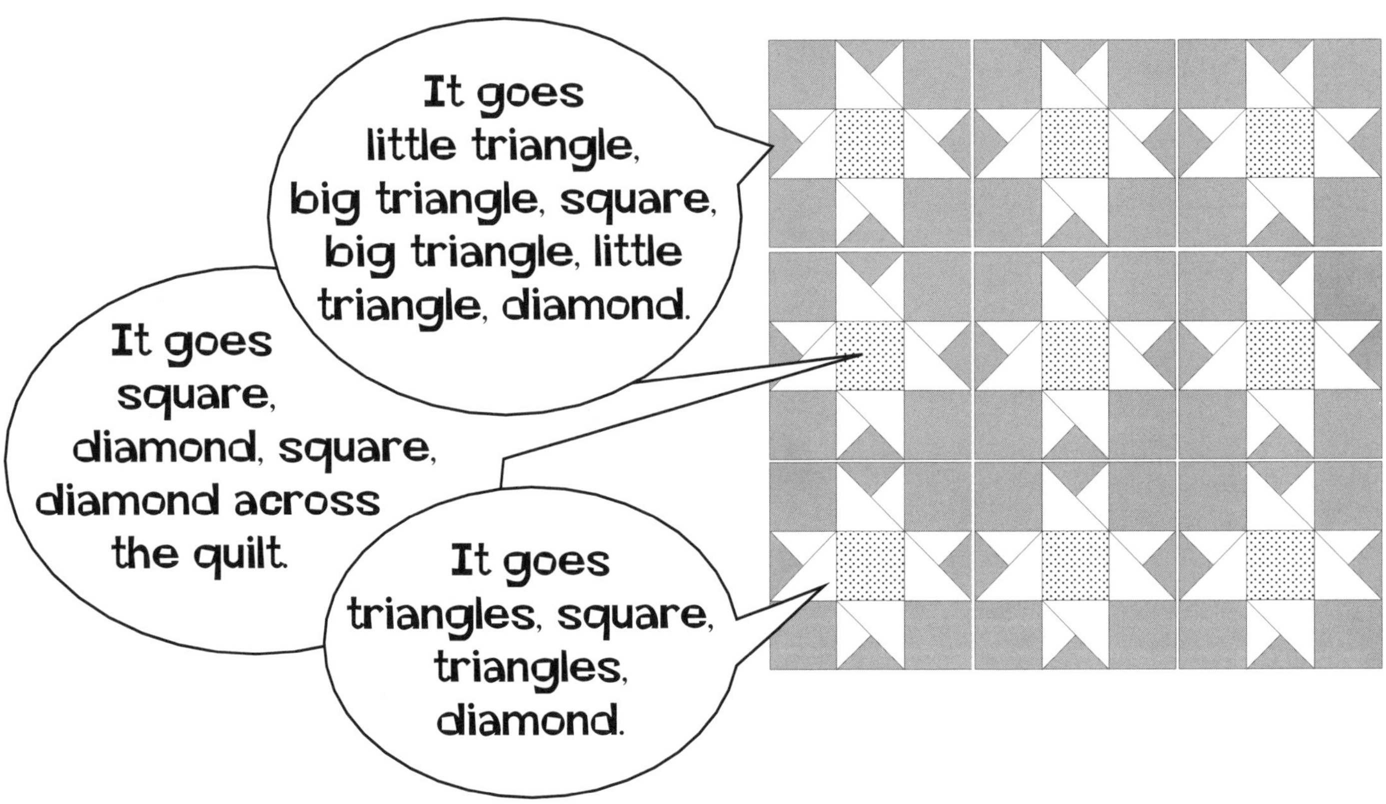

First graders try to be as different as possible. They look for the unusual.

Vanessa: *I see triangle, square, triangle in a diagonal row.*
David: *Four small squares come together to make a large square.*
Tony: *It goes square, fish mouth, square, square, fish mouth, square, square, fish mouth, square all around the edge of the whole quilt.*

First graders will notice any errors in the blocks. I encourage the children to see that imperfections only make our quilt unique, or different from all other quilts like it.

This is a language building activity as well as a mathematical one. If your students have trouble finding patterns, describe a pattern you see and ask if they can find it. This not only helps them know what to look for, but it also models for them any language they may be lacking to describe what they see.

Teacher: *I see small square, small square, big square, small square, small square, big square. Can you find my pattern?*
Nathaniel: *I see it. It goes crooked across the middle* (jumping up and pointing out the pattern).
Teacher: *That's it. That crooked way is called the diagonal. Can you trace the diagonal with your fingers in the air?* (The children trace.)

If I make a window frame by cutting a square hole the size of one quilt block in a larger piece of paper, it is possible to isolate and describe designs that we would not have seen otherwise.

Teacher: *If I frame off the blocks a little differently I can get new and different designs. What do you notice about these designs?*
Michael: *One looks like a T.*
David: *One makes big, middle-sized and small squares.*
Meredith: *I wonder what would happen if we made a quilt out of one of those squares?*

Note: Once you have determined the size of your quilt, you might need to make extra blocks to complete the checkerboard pattern.

Traffic Light Quilt

Lesson Synopsis

Use the optional discussion topics and activities to introduce the traffic light quilt.

The teacher and the class meet at the rug. The teacher introduces the traffic light quilt block that will form half of the quilt. The children explore the idea of area as they learn how to construct the block with the teacher's help. Then they go to the tables to make their own traffic light quilt blocks.

The teacher and the class meet again at the rug. The teacher introduces the face quilt block that will form the other half of the quilt. The children learn how to construct the block with the teacher's help. Then they go to the tables to make their own face quilt blocks.

When the glued blocks have dried, the children work with the teacher to create a checkerboard pattern. The quilt is glued on bulletin board paper.

The quilt is displayed on the wall, and the children discuss patterns they see in it.

Materials Needed

For the introduction (optional)

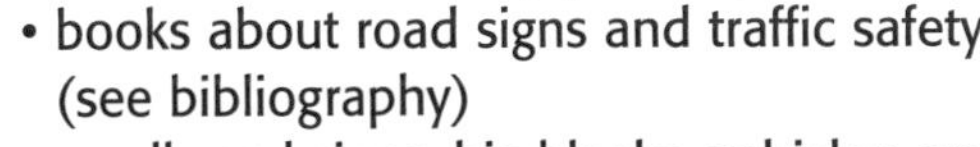

- books about road signs and traffic safety (see bibliography)
- small road signs, big blocks, vehicles, and play people
- quilts brought from home

For the teacher and each child to make a traffic light quilt block

- one traffic light blackline, page 30
- six 2″ squares of blue construction paper
- three 2″ squares of gray construction paper
- three 1½″ diameter circles: one red, one yellow, one green
- scissors and glue

For the teacher and each child to make a face quilt block

- one 6″ square of blue construction paper
- one 5″ circle in appropriate skin color
- strands of yarn in appropriate hair color
- crayons
- scissors and glue

To assemble the quilt

- all the dry traffic light and face quilt blocks
- one color cube per child
- one large sheet of white bulletin board paper
- glue

Introducing the Quilt

Share books on road signs and traffic safety. Discuss ways the children can travel safely to school. Write their ideas on chart paper. Have the children act out the meaning of the different signs and traffic lights, and the right way to cross a street. You might also talk about bike safety and the importance of helmets.

Place a set of small road signs with your big blocks so the children can build roads, place signs, move vehicles, and practice crossing streets with play people.

If quilts were brought in to share, lay them on the rug. Discuss any patterns the children see. Talk about how the quilts were made and find out if any have special stories.

Tell them they are going to make a quilt out of paper instead of cloth, and that it will be a traffic light quilt.

Making the Traffic Light Quilt Block

Overview

- ▼ Introduce the traffic light blackline.
- ▼ Children learn how to construct a traffic light quilt block.
- ▼ Children make their own traffic light quilt blocks.

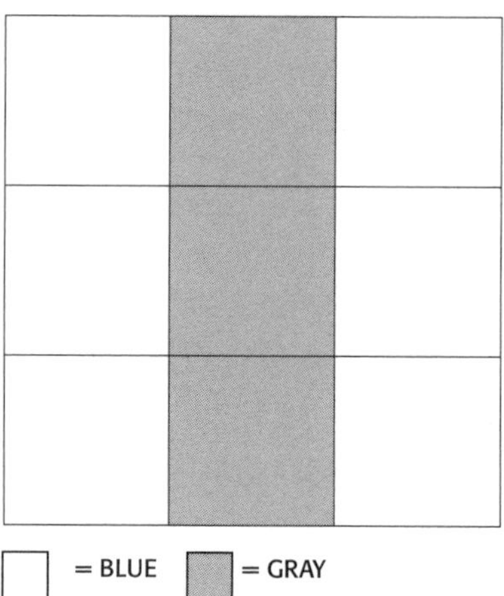

Have the 2″paper squares, $1\frac{1}{2}$″paper circles and blacklines on hand.

Gather the children at the rug. Give each child a traffic light blackline. Have volunteers describe what they see.

Children: *I see a lot of squares. Some of the squares are white and some are gray. There are six white squares and three gray squares. The gray squares go in a straight line down.*

Explore area as you help the children compute the number of squares of each color needed to cover the quilt block. See Early Experiences in Area, page 12, for this discussion.

Display a blue square. Explain that the blue squares belong on the white part of the blackline. Ask the children how many blue squares are needed to cover the white squares. Count out the number of blue squares suggested, and test their predictions.

Display a gray square. Explain that the gray squares belong on the shaded part of the blackline. Ask the children how many gray squares are needed, and test their predictions.

DON'T put glue on the tables until everyone has placed his or her pieces correctly.

Place the paper squares and scissors at the tables. Have the children go to their tables to place the squares correctly onto the traffic light blacklines.

Then distribute glue to the tables. When all the squares are glued in place, tell the children they are now going to turn their quilt blocks into traffic lights. Show them the red, yellow and green circles. Ask if they know which circle goes in the middle.

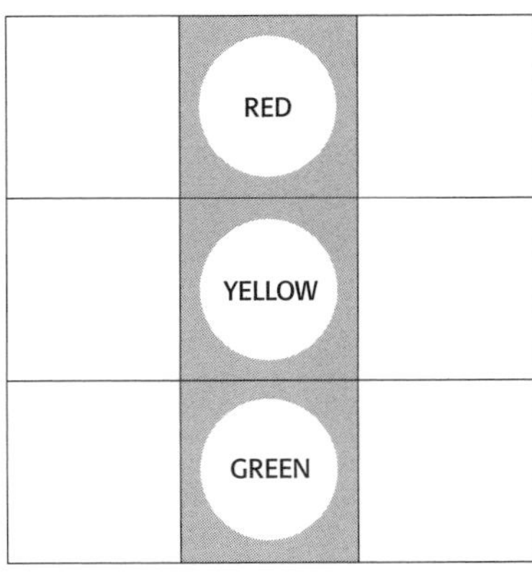

Children: *Yellow goes in the middle. Yeah, yellow is the middle one.*

Glue a yellow circle on the middle gray square.

Repeat the procedure with the red (top) and green (bottom) circles.

Place the colored circles at the tables. Have the children place the circles correctly onto their traffic lights, and glue them in place.

When the children have finished gluing all the circles in place, they should cut out their quilt blocks carefully around the edges so no white remains. Put the blocks aside to dry.

Step 2

Making the Face Quilt Block

Overview

- ▼ Demonstrate making a picture of your face on a quilt block.
- ▼ Children learn how to make their faces on quilt blocks.
- ▼ Children make their own face quilt blocks.

Have the 6″ paper squares, 5″ paper circles, scissors, yarn and crayons on hand.

Gather the children at the rug. Tell them they are going to make pictures of themselves on quilt blocks, but first they will help you make yours. Ask them to describe what you look like. Have them help you find the right color circle for your face. Glue that circle to a blue square. Ask the children to describe your eye color, and discuss with them where the eyes should go on the large circle. Use the crayons to draw the eyes. Ask what else you need to add to your face and draw those parts. Show the children how to cut and glue on the right color yarn for hair.

Place the paper squares and circles, yarn, crayons, and scissors at the tables. Have the children go to their tables to make their own face quilt blocks. Put the blocks aside to dry.

Step 3

Assembling the Quilt

Gather the children at the rug. Have the traffic light and face quilt blocks in separate piles.

Tell the children you are going to make the quilt in a checkerboard pattern. Explain that the pattern will be traffic light, face, traffic light, face.

Teacher: *Which block will come first in our traffic light, face, traffic light, face pattern?*
Melenate: *Traffic light.* (She places a traffic light block in the top left corner of the bulletin board paper.)
Teacher: *What comes next?*
Raymond: *Face.* (He places a face block next to the traffic light block.)
Teacher: (after five blocks have been placed) *We're going to stop and start a new row here* (pointing to the first space in the next row). *What block comes next?*
Alapate: *Face.* (He places a face block.)

Depending on the number of quilt blocks made by your class, you will need to decide how long to make each row. Figure it so you come up with a good sized rectangle. The number in each row must be odd to retain the checkerboard pattern. Example: For forty squares, a good rectangle would be five across by eight down.

Explore counting in multiples while assembling the quilt. See Counting (and Counting in Multiples), page 21, for this discussion.

Call on volunteers to place the quilt blocks on the bulletin board paper in the correct order. Have the class chant the pattern and count the blocks as each one is placed.

If you have leftover blocks, you can make them into pillows.

See Making Quilt Block Pillows, page 20, for how to turn leftover quilt blocks into a mini art project.

After all the quilt blocks have been placed correctly in a checkerboard design, glue them on the bulletin board paper, leaving a border.

Searching for Patterns and Designs

See Hidden Patterns and Designs, page 22, for a complete discussion of exploring patterns in finished quilts.

Hang the finished quilt on the wall for all to admire. Encourage the children to find designs and patterns hidden in the quilt. You may choose to record their comments on paper idea bubbles and attach them to the quilt.

There's a blue sky around my face!
The traffic lights go in a diagonal.
It's just like a checkerboard!

Traffic Light

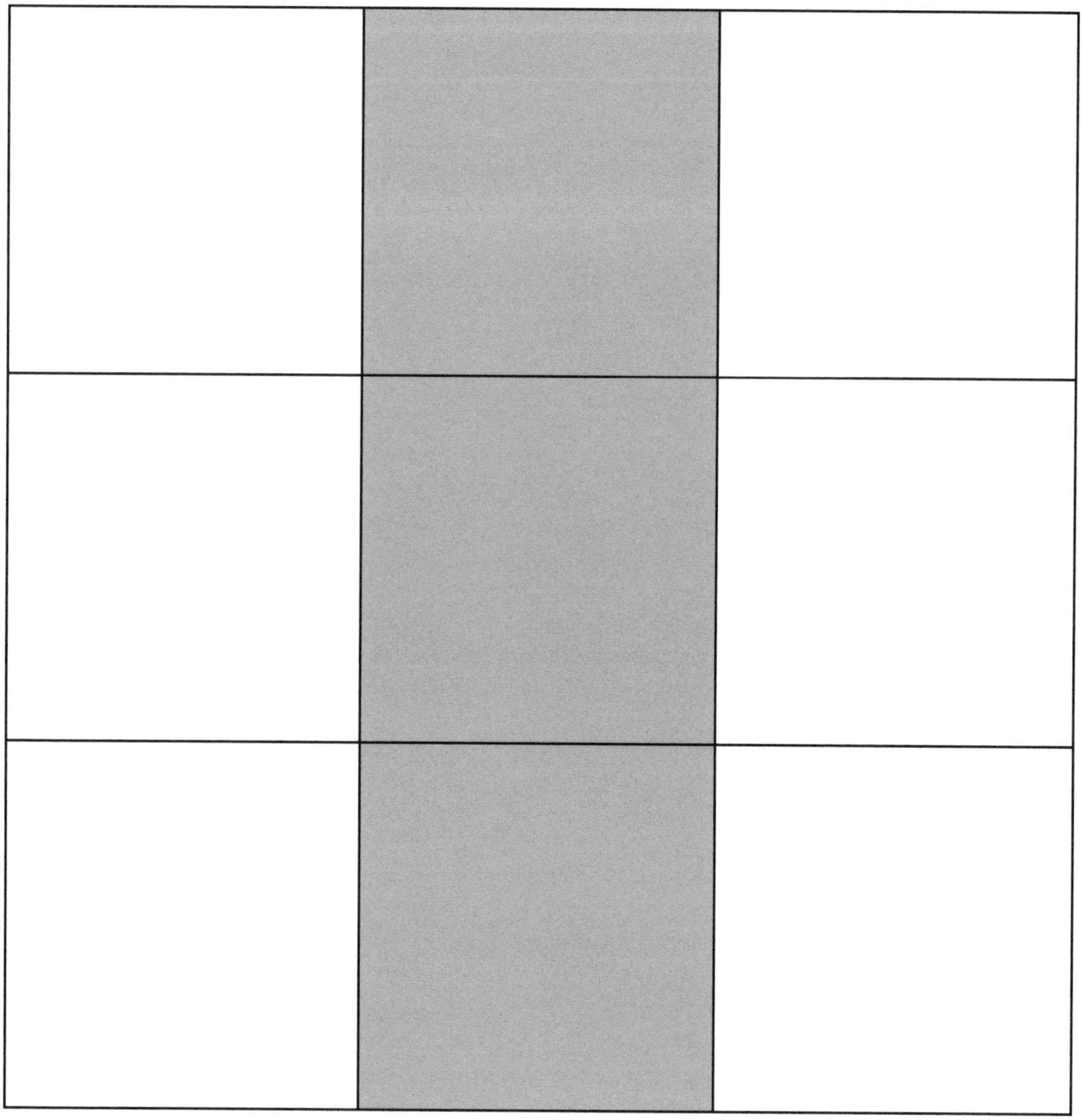

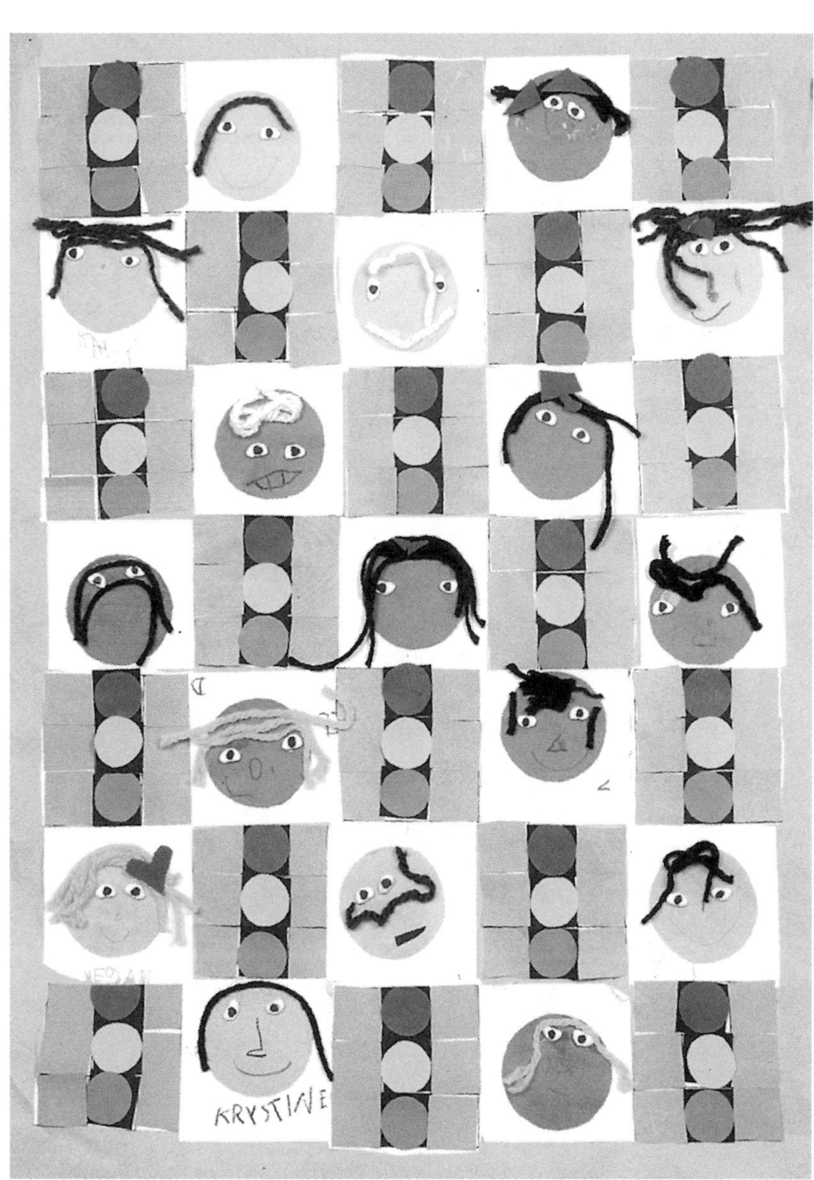

Traffic Light Quilt made by students from Sunnybrae School in San Mateo, California. See a color version of this quilt on the cover.

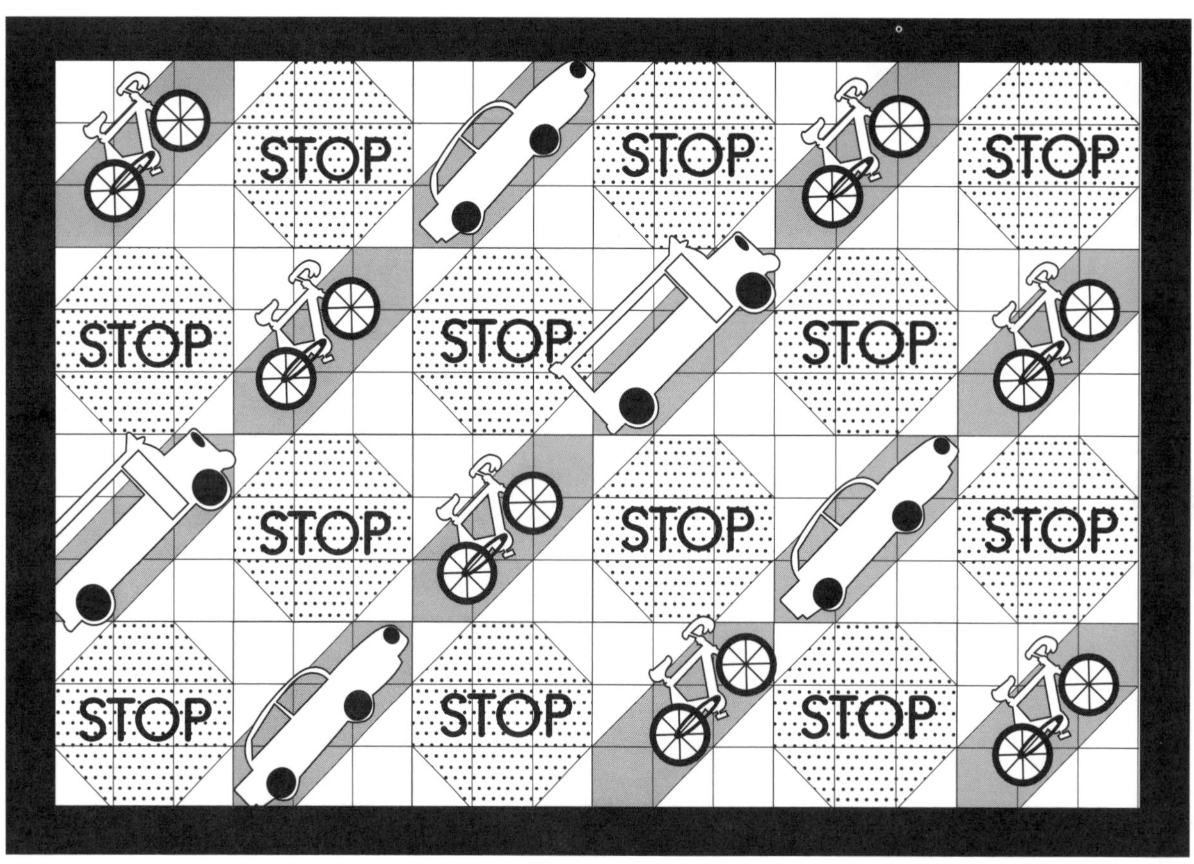

Note: Once the quilt design has been selected, you might need to make extra quilt blocks to complete a row.

Stop Sign Quilt

Lesson Synopsis / Materials Needed

Use the optional discussion topics and activities to introduce the stop sign quilt.

For the introduction (optional)
- books about road signs and traffic safety (see bibliography)
- quilts brought from home

The teacher and the class meet at the rug. The teacher introduces the stop sign quilt block that will form half of the quilt. The children explore the ideas of area and one-half as they learn how to construct the block with the teacher's help. Then they go to the tables to make their own stop sign quilt blocks.

For the teacher and each child to make a stop sign quilt block
- one stop sign blackline, page 39
- seven 2″ squares of red construction paper
- one 2″ square of green construction paper
- one 2″ square of gray construction paper
- scissors and glue
- chalk or a black crayon

The teacher and the class meet again at the rug. The teacher introduces the road quilt block that will form the other half of the quilt. The children explore the ideas of area and one-half as they learn how to construct the block with the teacher's help. Then they go to the tables to make a road quilt block and a paper vehicle to go on the road.

For the teacher and each child to make a road quilt block
- one road blackline, page 40
- five 2″ squares of gray construction paper
- four 2″ squares of green construction paper
- one 5″ x 3″ piece of assorted colored paper
- two 2″ squares of black construction paper
- one 3″ x 5″ piece of white paper
- scissors and glue

The children work in small groups to find patterns and shapes for the quilt using tiles equal to the number quilt blocks made by the class. They gather at the rug, share their solutions and select their favorite as the model for assembling the quilt. The quilt is assembled and glued on bulletin board paper.

For the teacher and each small group
- 1″ square tiles of one color equal to the number of stop sign quilt squares
- 1″ square tiles of another color equal to the number of road quilt squares

To assemble the quilt
- all the dry stop sign and road quilt blocks
- one color cube per child
- one large sheet of white or red bulletin board paper
- glue

The quilt is displayed on the wall, and the children discuss patterns they see in it.

Introducing the Quilt

Share books on road signs and traffic safety. Discuss ways children can travel safely to school. Write their ideas on chart paper. Have them act out the meaning of different road signs and traffic lights, including the right way to cross a street. You might also talk about bike safety and the importance of helmets.

If quilts were brought in to share, lay them on the rug. Discuss any patterns the children see. Talk about how the quilts were made and find out if any have special stories.

Tell the children they are going to make a class quilt out of paper instead of cloth. Tell them it will be a stop sign quilt.

Making the Stop Sign Quilt Block

Overview

▼ Introduce the stop sign blackline.
▼ Children learn how to construct a stop sign quilt block.
▼ Children make their own stop sign quilt blocks.

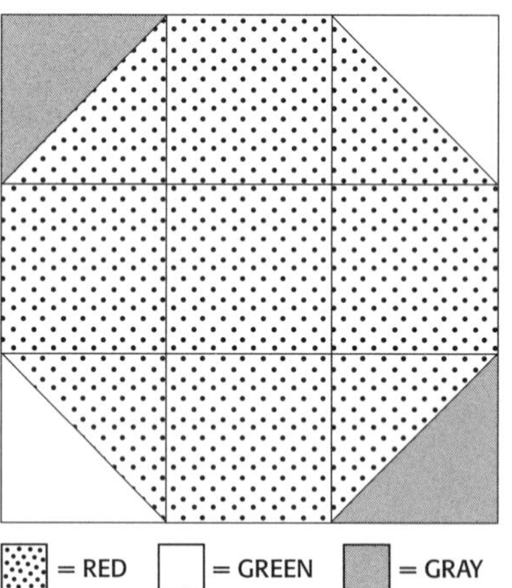

Have the 2″ paper squares, scissors and blacklines on hand.

Gather the children at the rug. Give each a stop sign blackline. Have volunteers describe what they see.

Children: *There are triangles and squares. Some are white and some are gray and some are dotted. It looks a little like a stop sign.*

Show the children your stop sign blackline and a red square. Ask if they can find where it goes.

Children: *It must go on the part with dots, because that's the part that looks like the stop sign.*

Explore the ideas that a square is made up of two triangles and that each triangle is half of the square. See Triangles and Halves, page 8, for this discussion.

Have children come up and place red squares until no more can be placed.

Teacher: *All we have left is this shape.* (She points to the dotted triangles.)

Explore area as you help the children compute the number of squares of each color needed to cover the quilt block. See Early Experiences in Area, page 12, for this discussion.

DON'T put glue on the tables until everyone has placed his or her pieces correctly.

Explain that you have no red triangles. Challenge the children to find a way to make triangles from a square. Ask them to figure out how many red squares they will need altogether to cover the stop sign. Have volunteers explain their reasoning. Count out the number of squares suggested and test their predictions.

Tell the children two of the corners will be covered with green triangles. Have them figure out the number of green squares needed for this and test their predictions. Repeat the procedure with the gray squares.

Place the paper squares and scissors at the tables. Have the children go to the tables to cut and place their squares correctly onto the stop sign blacklines.

Then distribute glue to the tables. When the children have finished gluing all the squares and triangles in place, they should cut out their quilt blocks carefully around the edges so no white remains. Put the blocks aside to dry.

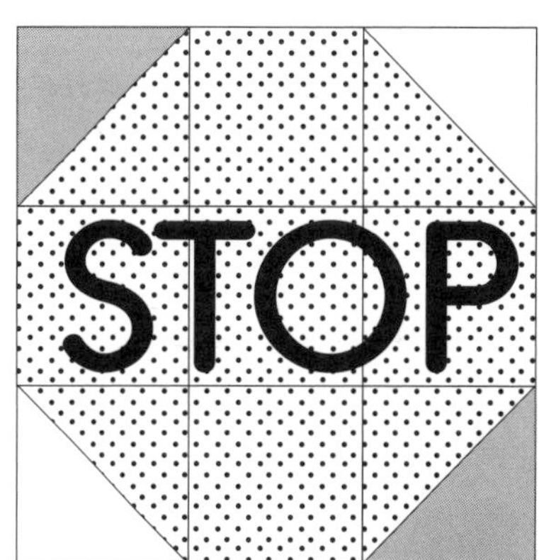

When the glued blocks have dried, distribute them to the children. Hold up a stop sign quilt block. Ask the children what the stop sign should say. Call on a volunteer to spell the word "STOP" as you write it across the middle of the stop sign with chalk or a black crayon.

Distribute the dried stop sign quilt blocks and chalk or crayons to the children. Have them write the word "STOP" on their blocks as shown. Then collect the blocks.

Step 2

Making the Road Quilt Block

Overview

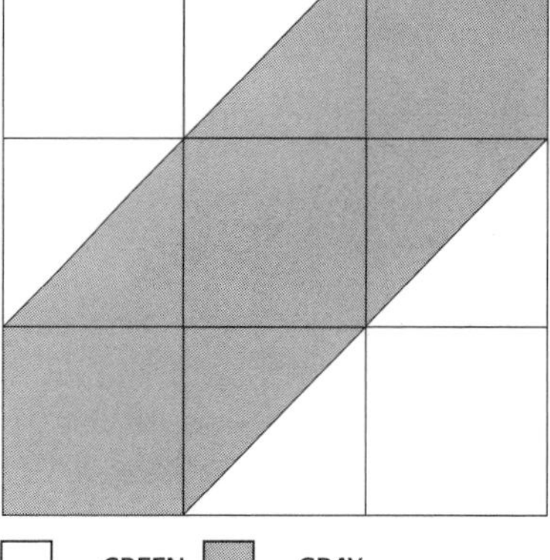

- ▼ Introduce the road blackline.
- ▼ Children learn how to construct a road quilt block and a paper vehicle.
- ▼ Children make their own road quilt blocks.

Have the 2″ paper squares, 5″ rectangles (or vehicle blacklines), scissors and road blacklines on hand.

Gather the children at the rug. Give each a road blackline. Have volunteers describe what they see.

Javier: *There are triangles and squares. Some are white and some are gray. It looks a little like a road.*
Teacher: *That's right. It is a road. We are going to use gray and green squares to cover the block. Where do you think the gray squares will go?*
Micheleen: *They must go on the gray squares, because that's the part that looks like the road, and a road is sort of gray.*

Display a gray square and point to one of the shaded triangles on the blackline. Explain that you have no triangles to cover it. Challenge the children to find a way to make triangles from the square.

Ask the children to figure out how many gray squares they will need altogether to cover the road. Have volunteers explain their reasoning.

Count out the number of squares suggested and test their predictions.

Explain that the green squares will cover the rest of the quilt block to look like grass. Have children figure out the number of green squares needed and test their predictions.

DON'T put glue on the tables until everyone has placed his or her pieces correctly.

Place the paper squares and scissors at the tables. Have the children go to their tables to cut and place their squares correctly onto the road blacklines.

Then distribute glue to the tables. When the children have finished gluing all the squares and triangles in place, they should cut out their quilt blocks carefully around the edges so no white remains. Put the blocks aside to dry.

When the glued blocks have dried, distribute them to the children. Hold up a road quilt block. Ask the children what could be found moving on the road.

Explain that they are going to cut out paper cars, buses, trucks, or bikes to go on their roads. Demonstrate how to make a simple vehicle using construction paper. (You may use the vehicle pattern blackline, page 41.) Have a volunteer place the vehicle on a road quilt block.

Place assorted colors of construction paper, glue, and scissors at the tables. Have each child make one vehicle and glue it onto his or her road quilt block.

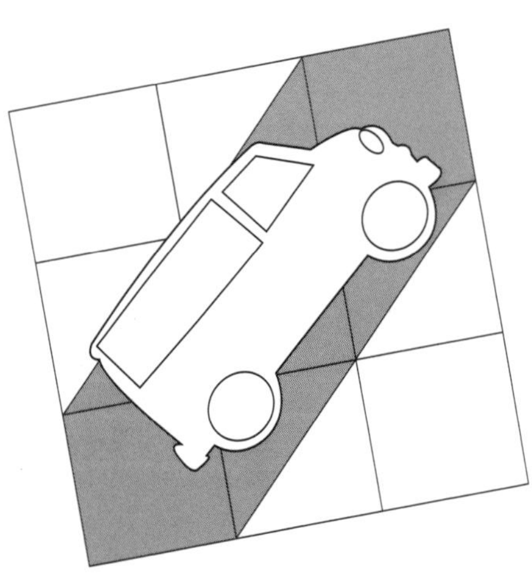

Step 3

Assembling the Quilt

Gather the children at the rug. Place all the finished quilt blocks in the center of the rug. Ask the children how many quilt blocks they think there are.

Jose: *We each made two. So I think there will be about thirty.*
Stephanie: *I think there are more than thirty. There are twenty of us. 20 + 20 = 40. There are forty quilt blocks.*
Jeff: *Yeah. There are forty.*
Javier: *Let's count them.*

Count the quilt blocks together. Then tell the children you are going to count out the same number of tiles. Explain that they will use the tiles to decide on a good shape and pattern for the quilt. Remind them that there are two different kinds of blocks in the quilt. Tell them to show this by using two different colors of tiles.

Explore shape and size. See Computing the Size of the Quilt, page 17, for this discussion.

Sometimes the number of quilt blocks does not easily lend itself to a good quilt shape. Brainstorm with the children what might be done to solve this problem. Some possible solutions are to make more quilt blocks until there are enough to make a good shape, to use left over quilt blocks to make pillows, to leave out the four blocks in the corners so the quilt will "lay right" on the bed, or to make two smaller quilts instead of one large one.

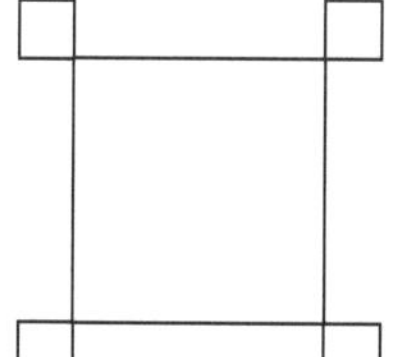
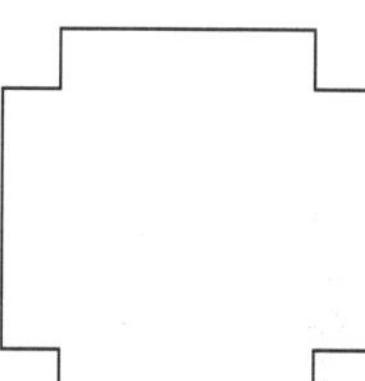

An example: For forty-eight blocks a good rectangle would be 5 x 9, with three blocks left over to make a pillow.

Divide the children into small groups. Four in each group is best. Give each group tiles (half in one color, half in another color). Have each group experiment to find a good shape for the quilt. (Don't worry about pattern at this point.) Ask each group to share its favorite shape. Choose one of the shapes for the class's quilt.

Next ask all the groups to arrange their tiles in the selected shape and experiment to find a good pattern for the tiles.

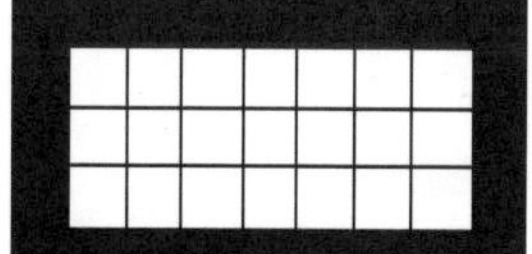

As the children come up with ideas, let them use the quilt blocks to test their plans. Some patterns look better with the quilt blocks than with the tiles.

Explore counting in multiples while assembling the quilt. See Counting (and Counting in Multiples), page 21, for this discussion.

Ask each group to arrange its favorite design in the center of the rug. Give each child a color cube. Explain that each person may cast one vote for his or her favorite design by placing a color cube on that design.

Assemble the pattern, counting aloud until all the blocks have been placed. The rows can be counted in multiples. Glue the blocks to the bulletin board paper, leaving a border.

Step 4

Searching for Patterns and Designs

See Hidden Patterns and Designs, page 22, for a complete discussion of exploring patterns in finished quilts.

Hang the finished quilt on the wall for all to admire. Encourage the children to find designs and patterns hidden in the quilt. You may choose to record their comments on paper idea bubbles and attach them to the quilt.

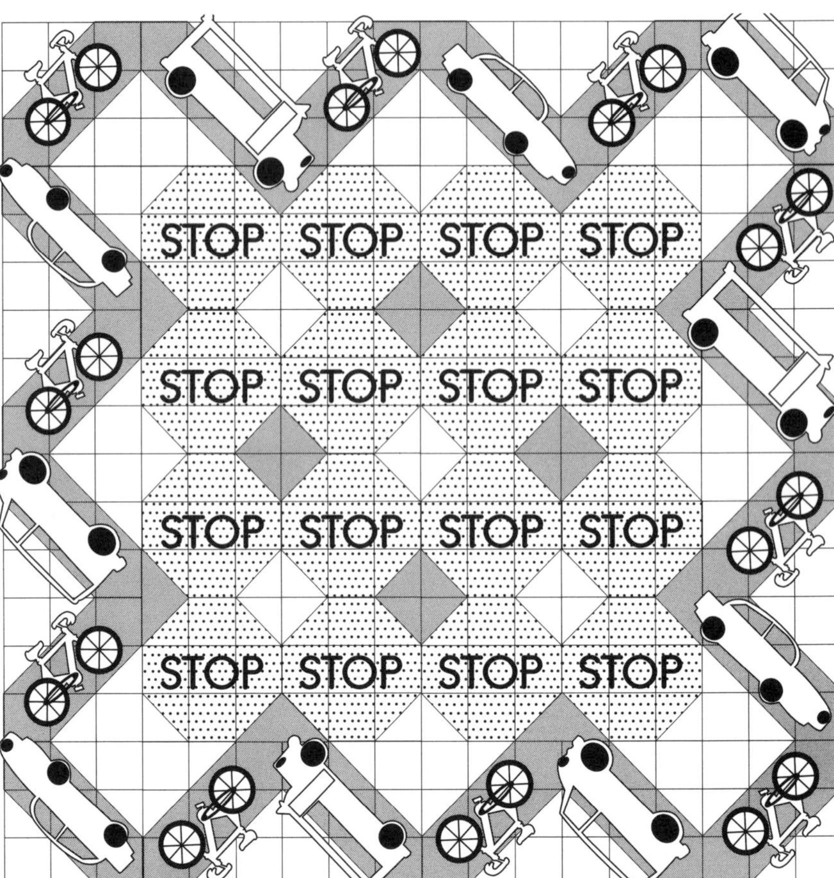

There are vehicles around the outside.

I see big triangles.

The roads are all connected.

Stop Sign

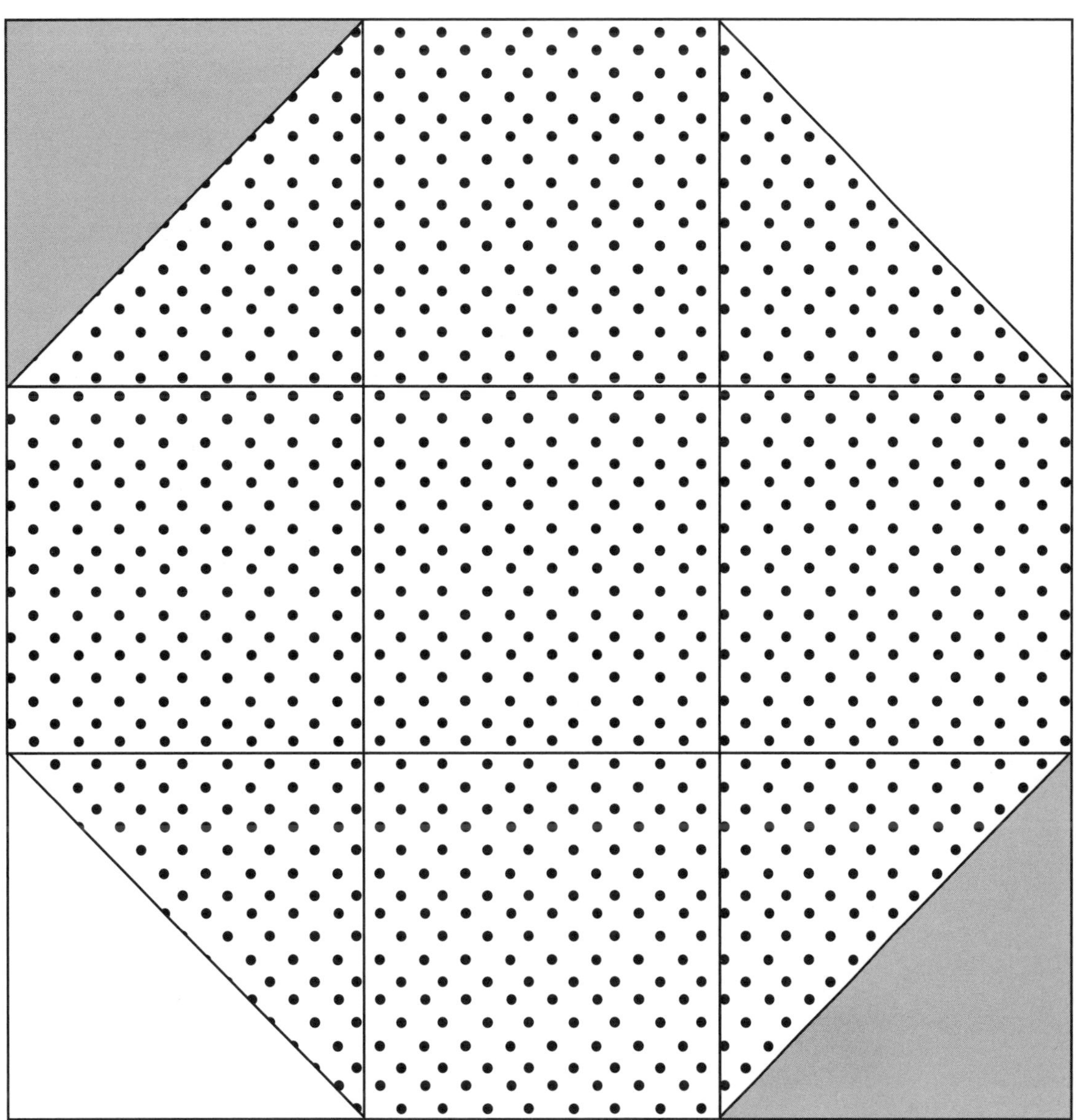

Road

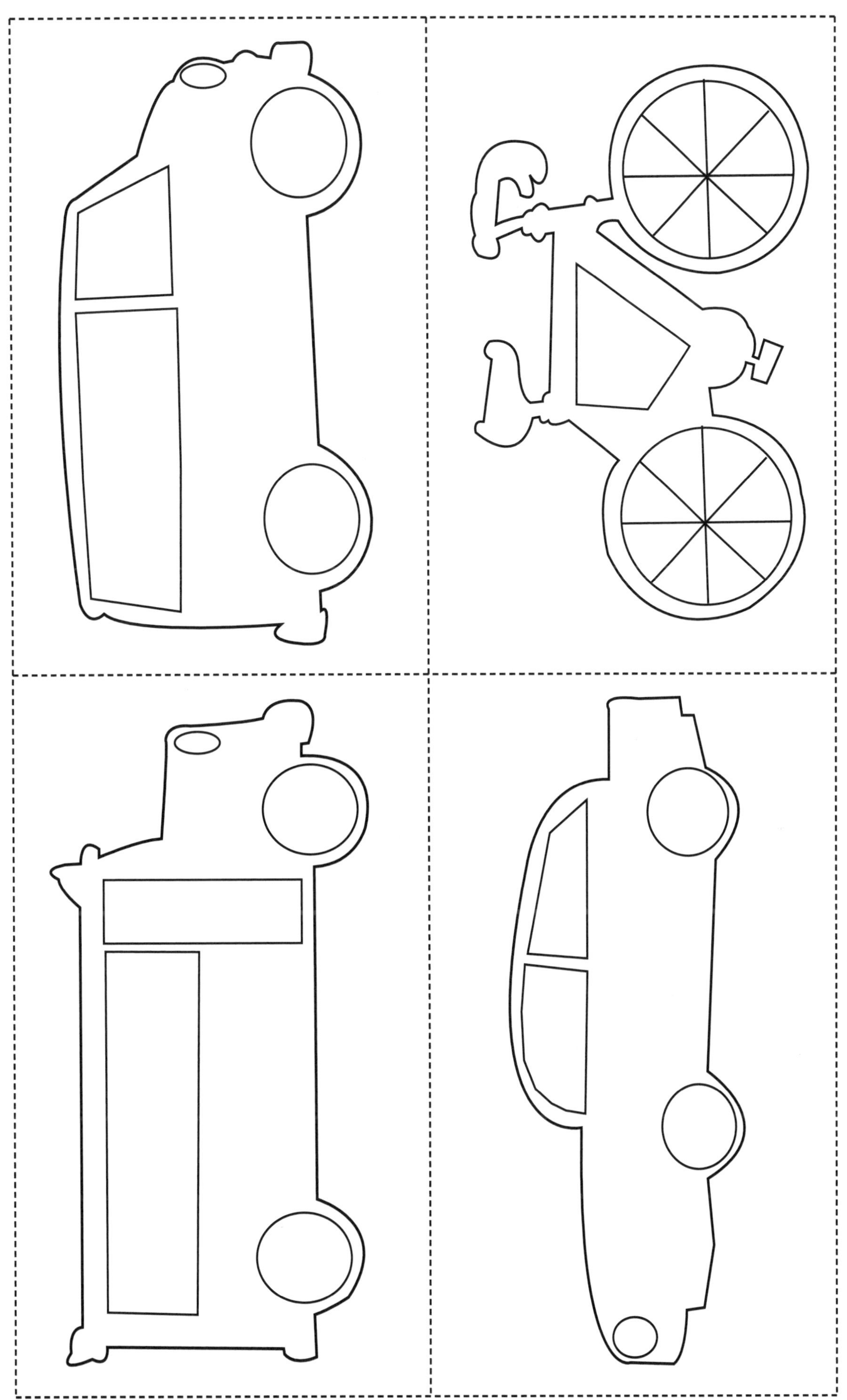

Samples of vehicles for use with the road quilt block.

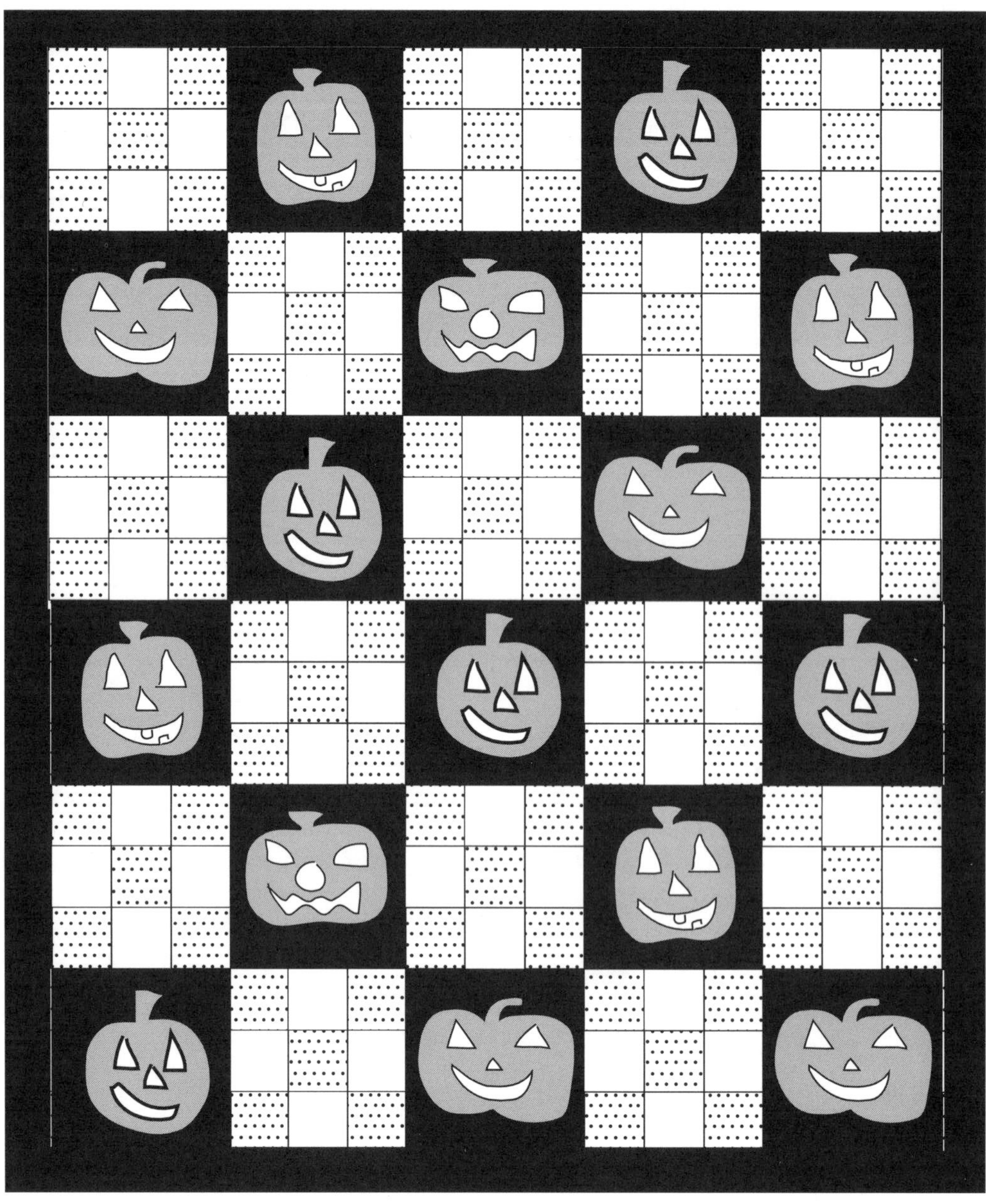

Note: Once you have determined the size of your quilt, you might need to make extra blocks to complete the checkerboard pattern.

Jack-O'-Lantern Quilt

Lesson Synopsis

Materials Needed

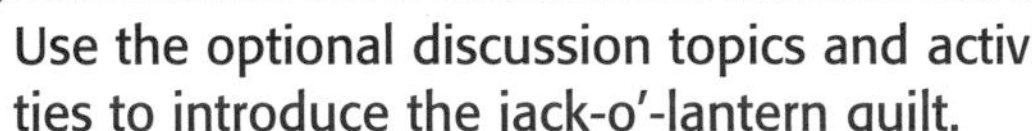

Use the optional discussion topics and activities to introduce the jack-o'-lantern quilt.

For the introduction (optional)
- *The Pumpkin Blanket* by Deborah Turney Zagwÿn
- quilts brought from home

Step 1

The teacher and the class meet at the rug. The teacher introduces the jack-o'-lantern quilt block that will form half of the quilt. The children learn how to construct a jack-o'-lantern with the teacher's help. Then they go to the tables to make their own jack-o'-lantern quilt blocks.

For the teacher and each child to make a jack-o'-lantern quilt block
- one 6″ square of orange construction paper
- one 6″ square of black construction paper
- crayons
- scissors and glue

Step 2

The teacher and the class meet again at the rug. The teacher introduces the checkerboard quilt block that will form the other half of the quilt. The children explore the ideas of area and one-half as they learn how to construct the block with the teacher's help. Then they go to the tables to make their own checkerboard quilt blocks.

For the teacher and each child to make a checkerboard quilt block
- one checkerboard blackline, page 47
- five 2″ squares of black construction paper
- four 2″ squares of orange construction paper
- scissors and glue

Step 3

When the glued blocks have dried, the children work with the teacher to create a checkerboard pattern. The quilt is glued on bulletin board paper.

To assemble the quilt
- all the dry jack-o'-lantern and checkerboard quilt blocks
- one large sheet of orange bulletin board paper
- glue

Step 4

The quilt is displayed on the wall, and the children discuss patterns they see in it.

Introducing the Quilt

Meet with the class to read and discuss *The Pumpkin Blanket* by Deborah Turney Zagwÿn. Ask questions about the story: Why does the child have to cut up her quilt? Why does she agree to cut it up? Does the quilt help the pumpkins grow? What happens to the quilt at the end of the story? Why do you think the child is not sad to lose her quilt?

You might also visit a pumpkin patch so the children can see how pumpkins are grown. Consider having the children plant their own pumpkin seeds so they can see this firsthand.

Tell the children they are going to make a paper jack-o'-lantern quilt.

Making the Jack-O'-Lantern Quilt Block

Overview

- ▼ Children learn how to construct a jack-o'-lantern quilt block.
- ▼ Children draw, cut and design their own jack-o'-lanterns and glue them onto black paper squares to make quilt blocks.

Have the 6" paper squares, scissors and crayons on hand.

Gather the children at the rug. Tell them they are going to make jack-o'-lanterns to go on the quilt. Show them a piece of orange paper. Ask what shape should be cut out of it to make the pumpkin. Ask what goes on top of the pumpkin. Model drawing and cutting out a simple pumpkin with a stem. Tell them that their pumpkins must be as large as possible.

Tell the children they will use crayons to turn their pumpkins into jack-o'-lanterns. Ask what the pumpkin needs to make it into a jack-o'-lantern (a face). Demonstrate drawing a face on the pumpkin. Encourage suggestions about what should be drawn.

Place the paper squares, crayons and scissors at the tables. Have the children work at the tables to make their jack-o'-lanterns.

When the jack-o'-lanterns are completed, place the black paper squares and glue at the tables. Have the children glue their jack-o'-lanterns on the black squares to make quilt blocks. Set the quilt blocks aside to dry.

Step 2

Making the Checkerboard Quilt Block

Overview

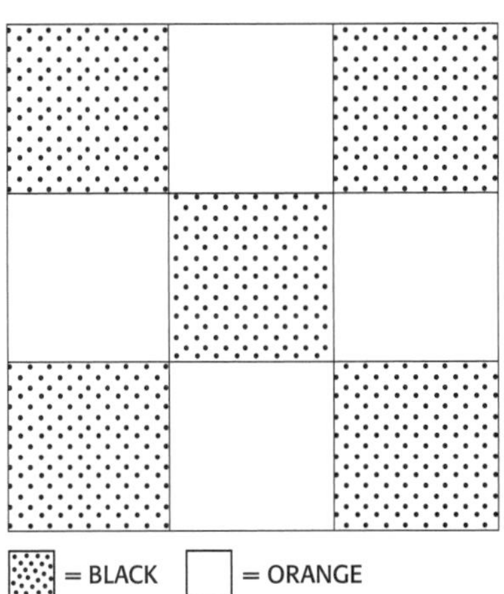

- ▼ Introduce the checkerboard blackline.
- ▼ Children learn how to construct a checkerboard quilt block.
- ▼ Children make their own checkerboard quilt blocks.

Have the 2" paper squares and blacklines on hand.

Gather the children at the rug. Give each a checkerboard blackline. Have volunteers describe what they see.

Children: *It looks like a checkerboard. It is in a pattern. Dotted square, white square, dotted square. All the shapes are squares. There are nine squares. Four squares are white. Five squares have dots.*

Explore area as you help the children compute the number of squares of each color needed to cover the quilt block. See Early Experiences in Area, page 12, for this discussion.

Display the four orange and five black squares. Ask the children where they think the two colors should be placed, and have them explain their reasoning. Place the orange and black squares as suggested.

Have the children compare the number of orange squares to the number of black squares.

DON'T put glue on the tables until everyone has placed his or her pieces correctly.

Place the paper squares (one color at a time) and scissors at the tables. Have the children go to their tables to place the squares correctly onto the checkerboard blacklines. Once they have placed the first color, put out the second color.

Then distribute glue to the tables. When the children have finished gluing all the squares in place, they should cut out their quilt blocks carefully around the edges so no white remains. Put the quilt blocks aside to dry.

Step 3

Assembling the Quilt

Gather the children at the rug. Have the jack-o'-lantern and checkerboard quilt blocks in separate piles.

Tell the children you are going to make the quilt in a checkerboard pattern. Ask if anyone knows what that is. Ask a volunteer to demonstrate, or if no one knows, explain that the pattern could be checkerboard, jack-o'-lantern, checkerboard, jack-o'-lantern. Ask for a volunteer to show which block will come first.

Jessica: *I think the checkerboard will come first.* (She places a checkerboard block in the top left corner of the bulletin board paper.)
Teacher: *What comes next?*
Tony: *Jack-o'-lantern.* (He places a jack-o'-lantern block next to the checkerboard block.)

Explore counting in multiples while assembling the quilt. See Counting (and Counting in Multiples), page 21, for this discussion.

Call on volunteers to place the rest of the blocks on the bulletin board paper in the correct order. Have the class chant the pattern and count the blocks as each one is placed. Make sure to have an odd number of blocks in each row. For example, if you have forty-eight blocks, a good quilt size would be a 5 x 9 rectangle, with three blocks left over.

See Making Quilt Block Pillows, page 20, for how to turn leftover quilt blocks into a mini art project.

If you have leftover blocks, you can make them into pillows.

After all the quilt blocks have been placed correctly in a checkerboard design, glue them on the bulletin board paper, leaving a border.

Searching for Patterns and Designs

See Hidden Patterns and Designs, page 22, for a complete discussion of exploring patterns in finished quilts.

Hang the finished quilt on the wall for all to admire. Encourage the children to find designs and patterns hidden in the quilt. You may choose to record their comments on paper idea bubbles and attach them to the quilt.

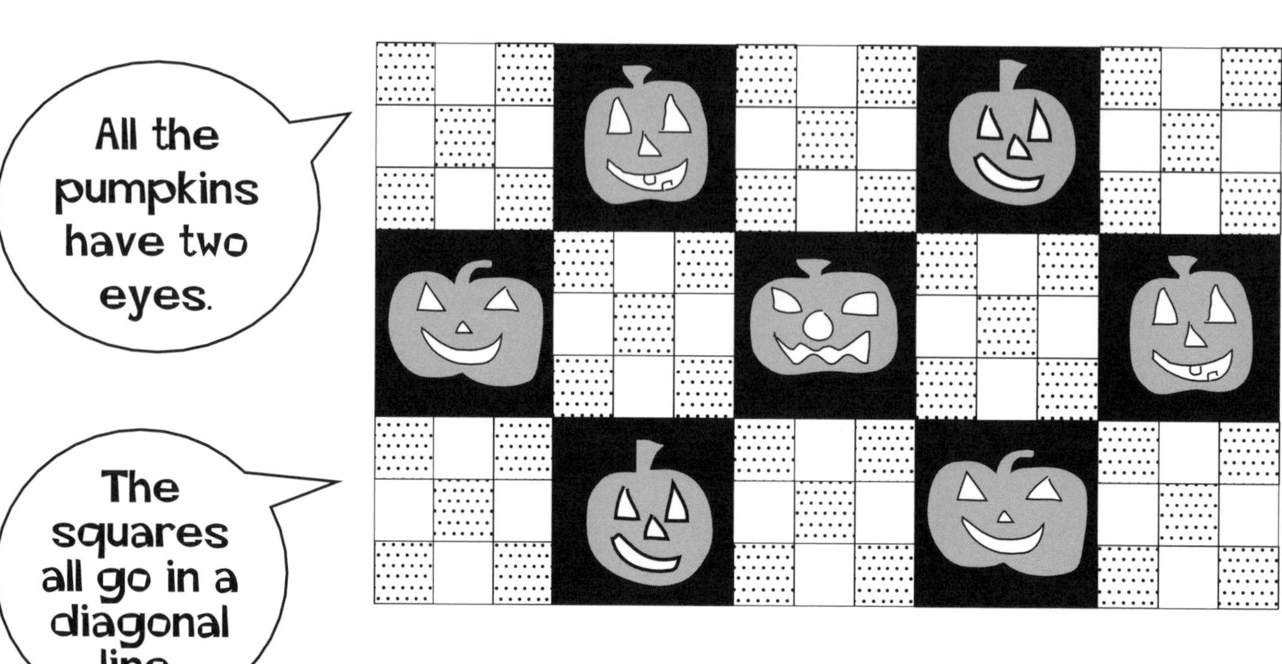

All the pumpkins have two eyes.
The squares all go in a diagonal line.

Checkerboard

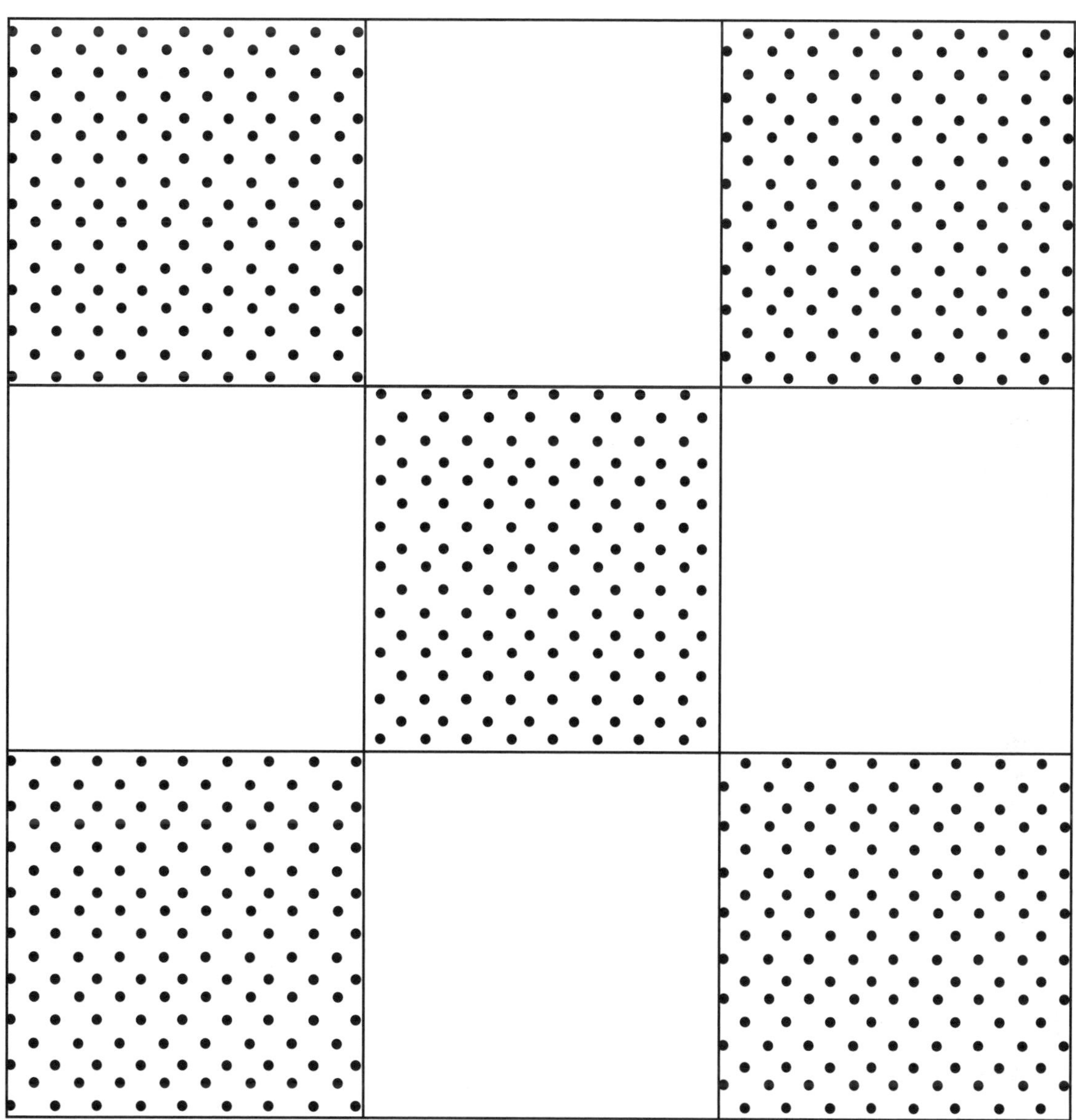

Note: This quilt is assembled from four-block squares. You will need a number of quilt blocks that is divisible by eight (16, 24, 32, etc.). You might need to make extra blocks.

Pumpkin Quilt

Lesson Synopsis

Use the optional discussion topics and activities to introduce the pumpkin quilt.

The teacher and the class meet at the rug. The teacher introduces the pumpkin quilt block that will form the quilt. The children explore the ideas of area and one-half as they learn how to construct the block with the teacher's help. Then they go to the tables to make their own pumpkin quilt blocks.

When the glued blocks have dried, the children work in small groups to find different patterns in a four-block quilt square. They gather at the rug, share their patterns, and select their favorite. The quilt is assembled from multiples of the selected square and glued on bulletin board paper.

The quilt is displayed on the wall, and the children discuss patterns they see in it.

Materials Needed

For the introduction (optional)
- *The Pumpkin Blanket* by Deborah Turney Zagwÿn
- quilts brought from home

For the teacher and each child to make a pumpkin quilt block
- one pumpkin blackline, page 53
- four 2″ squares of orange construction paper
- one 2″ square of green construction paper
- four 2″ squares of yellow construction paper
- scissors and glue

To assemble the quilt
- all the dry pumpkin quilt blocks
- one color cube per child
- one large sheet of black bulletin board paper
- glue

Introducing the Quilt

Read and discuss *The Pumpkin Blanket* by Deborah Turney Zagwÿn. Why was is it necessary for the child to cut up her quilt? Why did she agree to cut it up? Did the quilt help the pumpkins grow? What happened to the quilt at the end of the story? Why do you think the child was not sad to lose her quilt?

You might also visit a pumpkin patch so the children can see how pumpkins are grown. Consider having the children plant their own pumpkin seeds so they can see this firsthand.

Tell the children they are going to make a paper pumpkin quilt.

Making the Pumpkin Quilt Block

Overview

- ▼ Introduce the pumpkin blackline.
- ▼ Children learn how to construct a pumpkin quilt block.
- ▼ Children make their own pumpkin quilt blocks.

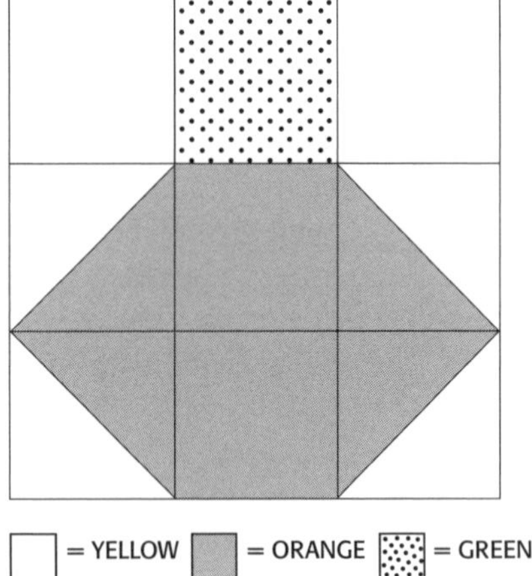

Have the 2″ paper squares, scissors and blacklines on hand.

Gather the children at the rug. Give each a pumpkin blackline. Have volunteers describe what they see.

Teacher: *What do you notice about this quilt block?*
Alan: *It looks like a strange pumpkin.*
Karin: *There are squares and triangles.*
Thomas: *There are three different colors: white, dotted, and gray.*
Teacher: (She holds up some orange squares.) *Where do you think the orange squares will go?*
Sean: *I think over the gray part, because that part is the pumpkin.*
Teacher: *What about the green square?*
David: *That will go at the top to make the stem.*
Teacher: *And the yellow squares?*
Rosa: *I think they'll go around the pumpkin. It will look like light.*

Point to a shaded triangle on the pumpkin blackline. Explain that you have no triangles to cover it. Challenge the children to find a way to make triangles from one of the orange squares.

Teach the ideas that a square is made up of two triangles and that each triangle is half of the square. See Triangles and Halves, page 10, for this discussion.

Explore area as you help the children compute the number of squares of each color needed to cover the quilt block. See Early Experiences in Area, page 12, for this discussion.

Ask the children to figure out how many orange squares they will need altogether to cover the pumpkin, and have volunteers explain their reasoning. Count out the number of squares suggested and test their predictions.

Repeat the procedure with the yellow squares.

Place the green square over the dotted square to look like a stem.

DON'T put glue on the tables until everyone has placed his or her pieces correctly.

Place the paper squares and scissors at the tables. Have the children go to their tables to cut and place their squares correctly onto the pumpkin blacklines.

Then distribute glue to the tables. When the children have finished gluing all the squares and triangles in place, they should cut out their quilt blocks carefully around the edges so no white remains. Put the blocks aside to dry.

Assembling the Quilt

To assemble this quilt you will need a total number of quilt blocks that is divisible by eight (16, 24, 32, etc.).

Divide the children into groups of four and give each group four of the finished pumpkin quilt blocks. Show them how to place the four blocks together to make a quilt square. Demonstrate rotating the blocks in different ways to create new designs.

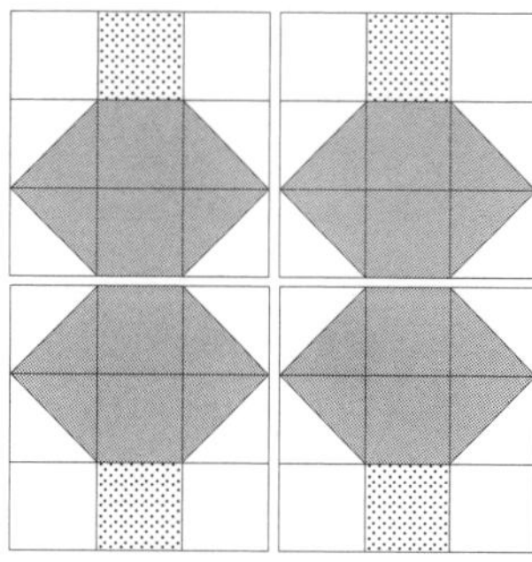

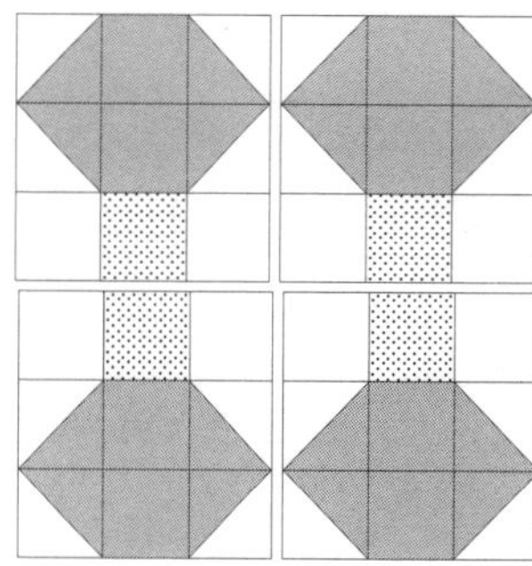

Help children discover patterns in the four-block quilt squares. See Slides and Rotations, page 14, for this discussion.

Encourage groups to experiment rotating the blocks to find a variety of designs. Allow time for the children to walk around and see other groups' designs.

Ask each group to arrange its favorite four-block design. Place all the groups' designs in the center of the rug. Give each child a color cube. Explain that each person may cast one vote for his or her favorite design by placing a color cube on that design. Each group then builds the selected quilt square from its four blocks.

See Making Quilt Block Pillows, page 20, for how to turn leftover quilt blocks into a mini art project.

If you have leftover blocks, you can make them into pillows.

Arrange all the quilt squares on the bulletin board paper to make the finished design. Glue them on the bulletin board paper, leaving a border.

Searching for Patterns and Designs

Hang the finished quilt on the wall for all to admire. Encourage the children to find designs and patterns hidden in the quilt. You may choose to record their comments on paper idea bubbles and attach them to the quilt.

See Hidden Patterns and Designs, page 22, for a complete discussion of exploring patterns in finished quilts.

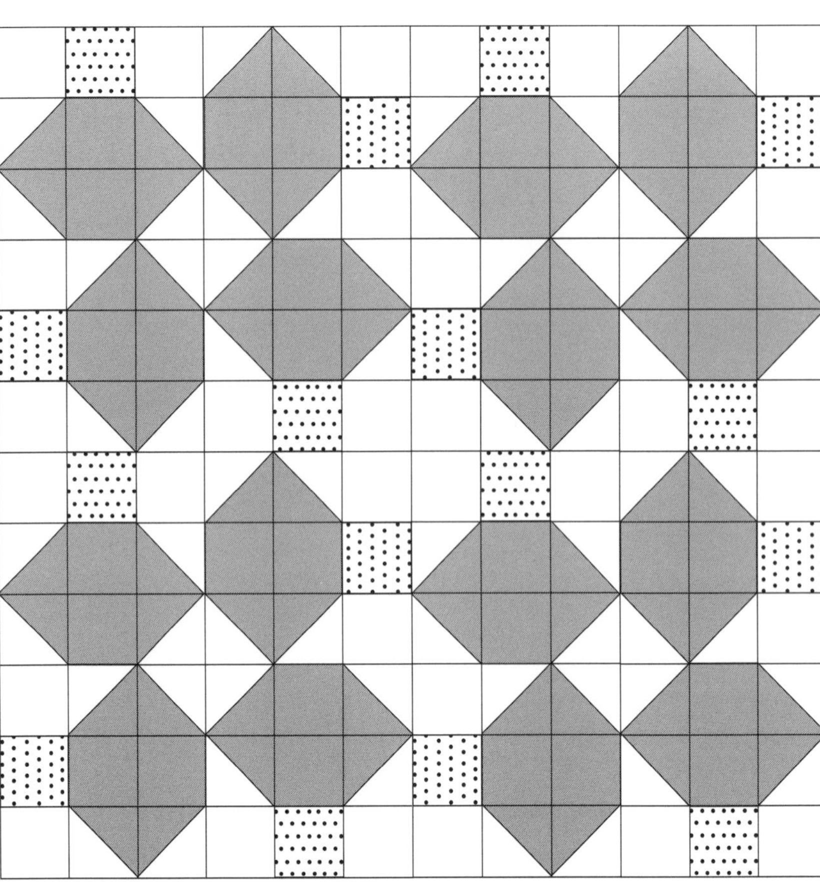

I see a yellow pinwheel right in the middle.
I see four yellow diamonds.
I see four big, orange flowers.

Pumpkin

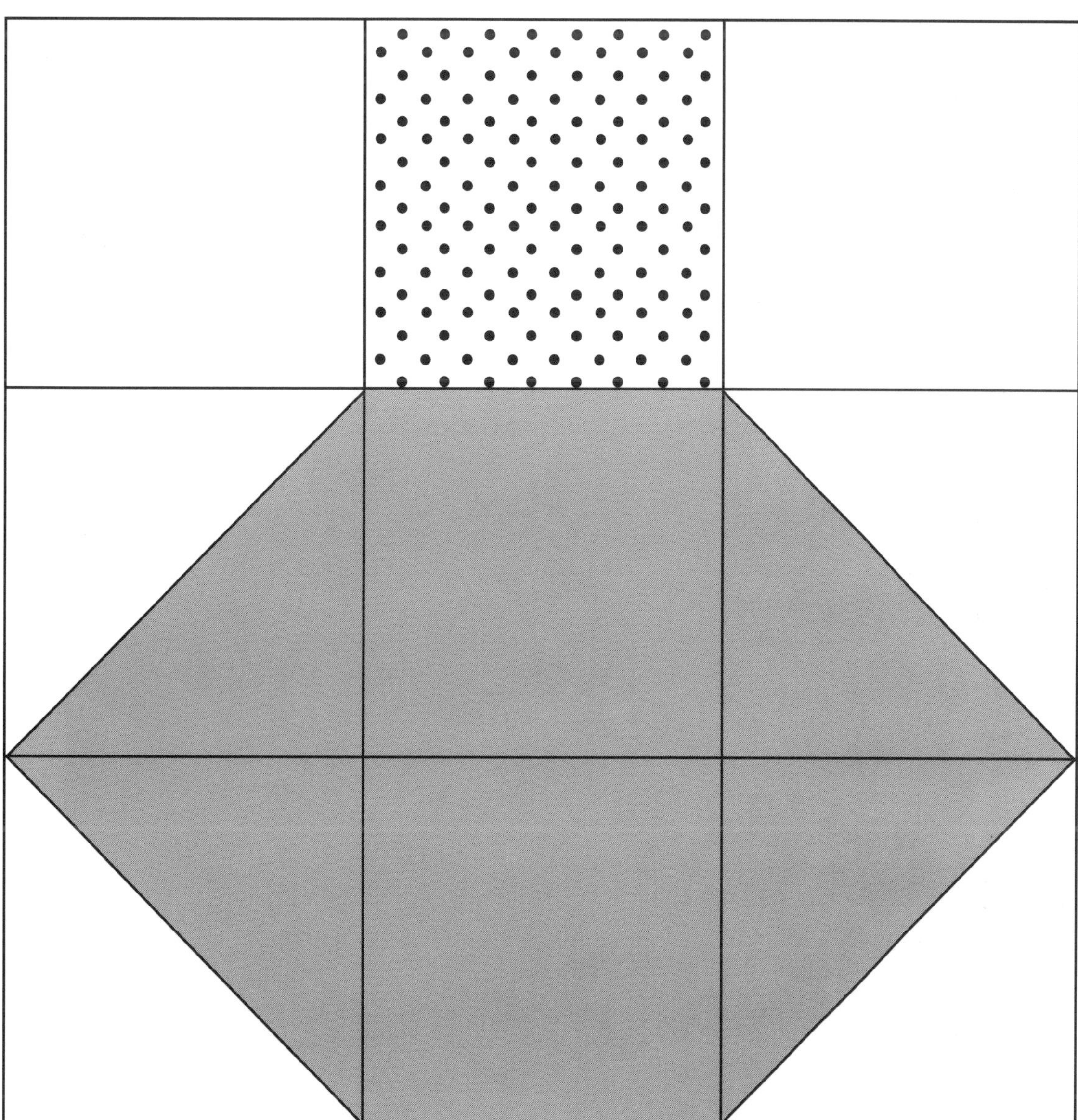

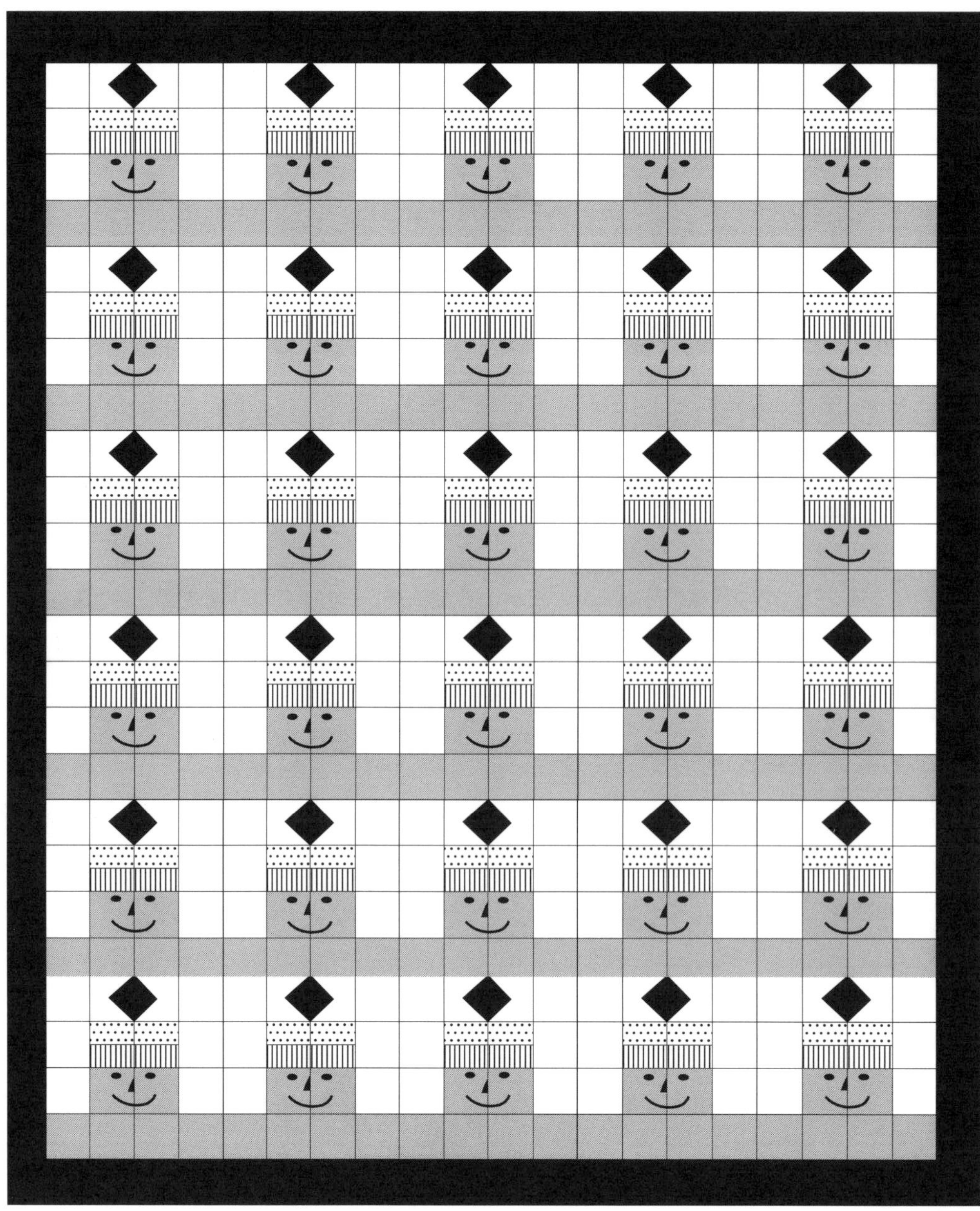

Note: Once the quilt design has been selected, you might need to make extra quilt blocks to complete a row.

Native American Quilt

Lesson Synopsis

Use the optional discussion topics and activities to introduce the Native American quilt.

The teacher and the class meet at the rug. The teacher introduces the Wampanoag boy quilt block that will form the quilt. The children explore the ideas of area and one-half as they learn how to construct the block with the teacher's help. Then they go to the tables to make their own Wampanoag boy quilt blocks.

When the glued blocks have dried, the children gather at the rug. The quilt is assembled and glued on bulletin board paper.

The quilt is displayed on the wall, and the children discuss patterns they see in it.

Materials Needed

For the introduction (optional)

- *Tapenum's Day: A Wampanoag Indian Boy in Pilgrim Times* by Kate Waters
- For extensive information about the Pilgrims and the native peoples they encountered, write to Plimoth Plantation, Inc., PO Box 1620, Plymouth, MA 02362, or call 1-800-262-9356.

For the teacher and each child to make a Wampanoag boy quilt block

- one Wampanoag boy blackline, page 59
- six 1½" squares of brown construction paper
- one 1½" square of black construction paper
- one 1½" square of red construction paper
- eight 1½" squares of light blue construction paper
- one 1" square of purple construction paper
- scissors and glue
- crayons

To assemble the quilt

- all the dry Wampanoag boy quilt blocks
- one large sheet of brown bulletin board paper
- glue

Curriculum Connections

Introducing the Quilt

Use this lesson as an opportunity to teach your class about the Native Americans who met the Pilgrims and to clear up misconceptions. The Native American people commonly described as part of a Thanksgiving unit are those that lived in teepees and rode horses. The native people the Pilgrims encountered around Plymouth, Massachusetts were from the Pokanoket tribe, a subgroup of the Wampanoag ("wam-pa-NO-og") that lived in reed and bark houses. They were farmers and hunters, and they lived in towns in the winter and near their farmland from the spring until fall. They continue to live in Massachusetts and Rhode Island today.

Read and discuss the book *Tapenum's Day: A Wampanoag Indian Boy in Pilgrim Times* by Kate Waters. Use the photographs to spark discussion: What is Tapenum's house like? How is it different from your house? Did he have his own bedroom? Is his bed like yours? How did Tapenum dress? Is that different from the way you dress? What did he eat? How did he get his food? Do you eat and get your food the same way? What things are important for Tapenum to learn to do? Are they the same things you need to learn? How is Tapenum like you?

The Wampanoags showed the Pilgrims how to plant, care for, harvest, and cook or prepare corn for eating. Discuss how important this plant was for both the Wampanoag and the Pilgrims. Bring in some ears of un-husked corn to share with the children. Plant corn in cups so they each have their own corn plants to take home. Prepare corn meal, corn pudding or corn bread.

Tell the children they are going to make a Wampanoag boy quilt to remind them of what they have learned.

Making the Quilt Block

Overview

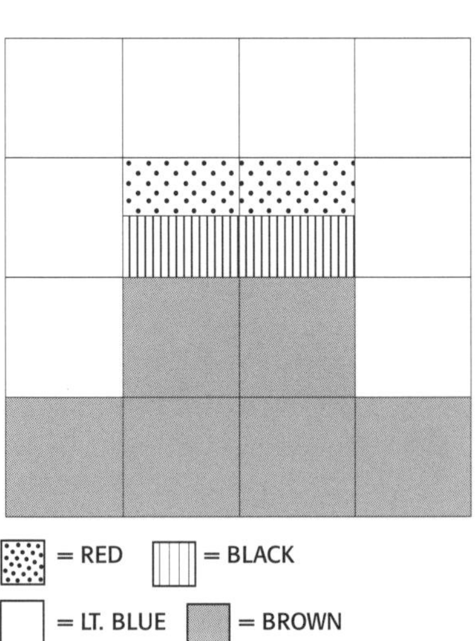

- ▼ Introduce the Wampanoag boy blackline.
- ▼ Children learn how to construct a Wampanoag boy quilt block.
- ▼ Children make their own Wampanoag boy quilt blocks.

Have the 1½″ paper squares, 1″ purple square, scissors and blacklines on hand.

Gather the children at the rug. Give each a Wampanoag boy blackline. Have volunteers describe what they see.

Alipate: *There are eight white squares.*
Richard: *There are six dark squares.*
Roxanne: *I see four rectangles. Two are dotted and two are striped.*
Heather: *I can see where his face goes.*

Show the children your Wampanoag boy blackline and the six brown, one black, one red, and eight light blue paper squares. Ask the children where they think they should be placed.

Explore area as you help the children compute the number of squares of each color needed to cover the quilt block. See Early Experiences in Area, page 12, for this discussion.

Teacher: *Where do you think the brown squares will go?*
Joshua: *I think they cover the gray squares to make his face.*
Teacher: *How many brown squares will you need to cover the face?*
Brittany: *I think we will need six squares. Look!* (She places the brown squares where they go.)
Teacher: *What about the black squares?*
Children: *They don't fit anywhere. They're too big.*
Thomas: *They are the wrong shape. We need rectangles.*

Explore the ideas that a square is made up of two rectangles and that each rectangle is half of the square. See Rectangles and Halves, page 10, for this discussion.

Point to one of the striped rectangles in the boy's headband. Explain that you have no rectangles to cover it. Hold up a black square. Challenge the children to find a way to make rectangles from the square.

Not all the children will see that one square makes two rectangles, and it's okay to assist them with this reasoning. They will revisit this idea often.

Have the children figure out the number of black squares needed and test their predictions. Repeat the procedure to cover the dotted rectangles with the red square.

Explain that the light blue squares will be used for the sky around the boy, covering all the white squares. Have the children figure out how many light blue squares they will need and test their predictions.

DON'T put glue on the tables until everyone has placed his or her pieces correctly.

Place all the paper squares (one color at a time) and scissors at the tables. Reserve the purple squares until the children are done gluing. Have the children go to their tables to cut and place the squares correctly onto the Wampanoag boy blacklines. Once they have placed the first color, put out the second color, and so on.

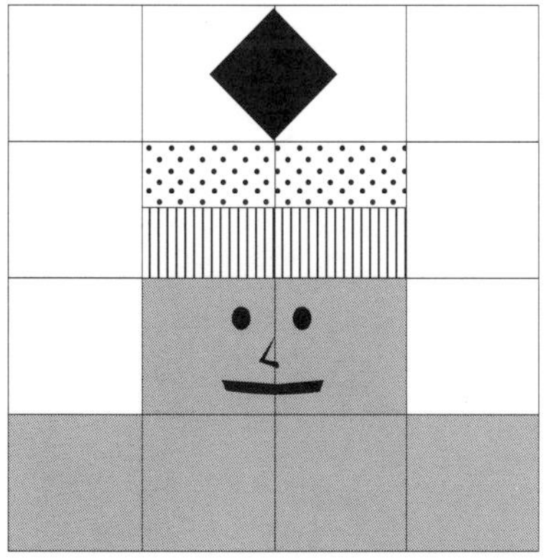

Then distribute glue to the tables. When the children have finished gluing all the squares and rectangles in place, give each one a purple square. Show them how to turn the square on the diagonal and glue it in place to make a feather in the headband.

Finally they should cut out their quilt blocks carefully around the edges so no white remains. Put the blocks aside to dry.

Distribute the dried Wampanoag boy quilt blocks and crayons to the children. Have them draw features on the boy's face.

Assembling the Quilt

Explore shape and size. See Computing the Size of the Quilt, page 17, for this discussion.

See Making Pillows, page 20, for how to turn leftover quilt blocks into a mini art project.

Explore counting in multiples while assembling the quilt. See Counting (and Counting in Multiples), page 21, for this discussion.

Gather the children at the rug. Place the brown bulletin board paper and the finished quilt blocks in the center of the rug. Tell the children they will decide on a good size and shape for the quilt.

Depending on the number of children in your room, you will need to decide how long to make each row of the quilt. Figure it so you arrive at a good sized rectangle or square. For example, if you have twenty blocks, your rectangle can be 5 x 4, with no extra blocks. For twenty-six blocks, your rectangle can be 6 x 4, with two extra blocks.

If you have leftover blocks, you can make them into pillows.

Lay out the first row of quilt blocks on the bulletin board paper, with help from the children. Have them predict how many blocks there will be after they add the second row. Encourage children to share their prediction strategies. As you place the blocks, have the children count aloud to check their predictions. Continue until the entire quilt is assembled.

Glue the finished quilt to the bulletin board paper, leaving a border.

Searching for Patterns and Designs

See Hidden Patterns and Designs, page 22, for a complete discussion of exploring patterns in finished quilts.

Hang the quilt on the wall for all to admire. Encourage the children to find designs and patterns hidden in the quilt. You may choose to record their comments on paper idea bubbles and attach them to the quilt.

It goes blue, purple, blue, purple across each row.

There is a long, brown line in each row.

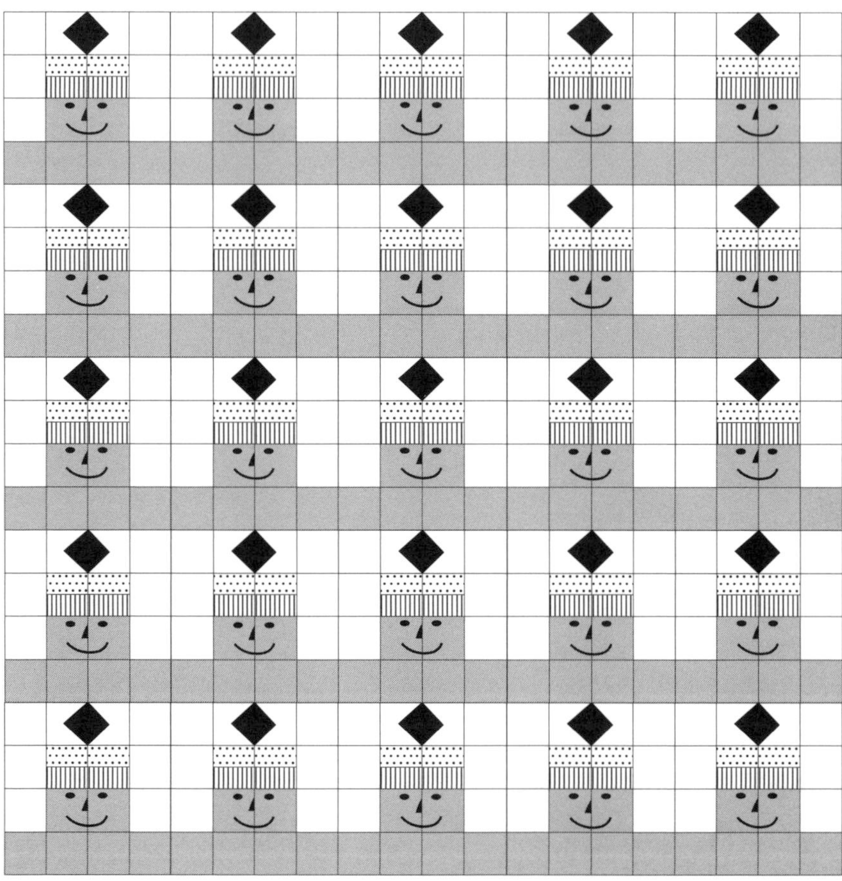

Wampanoag Boy

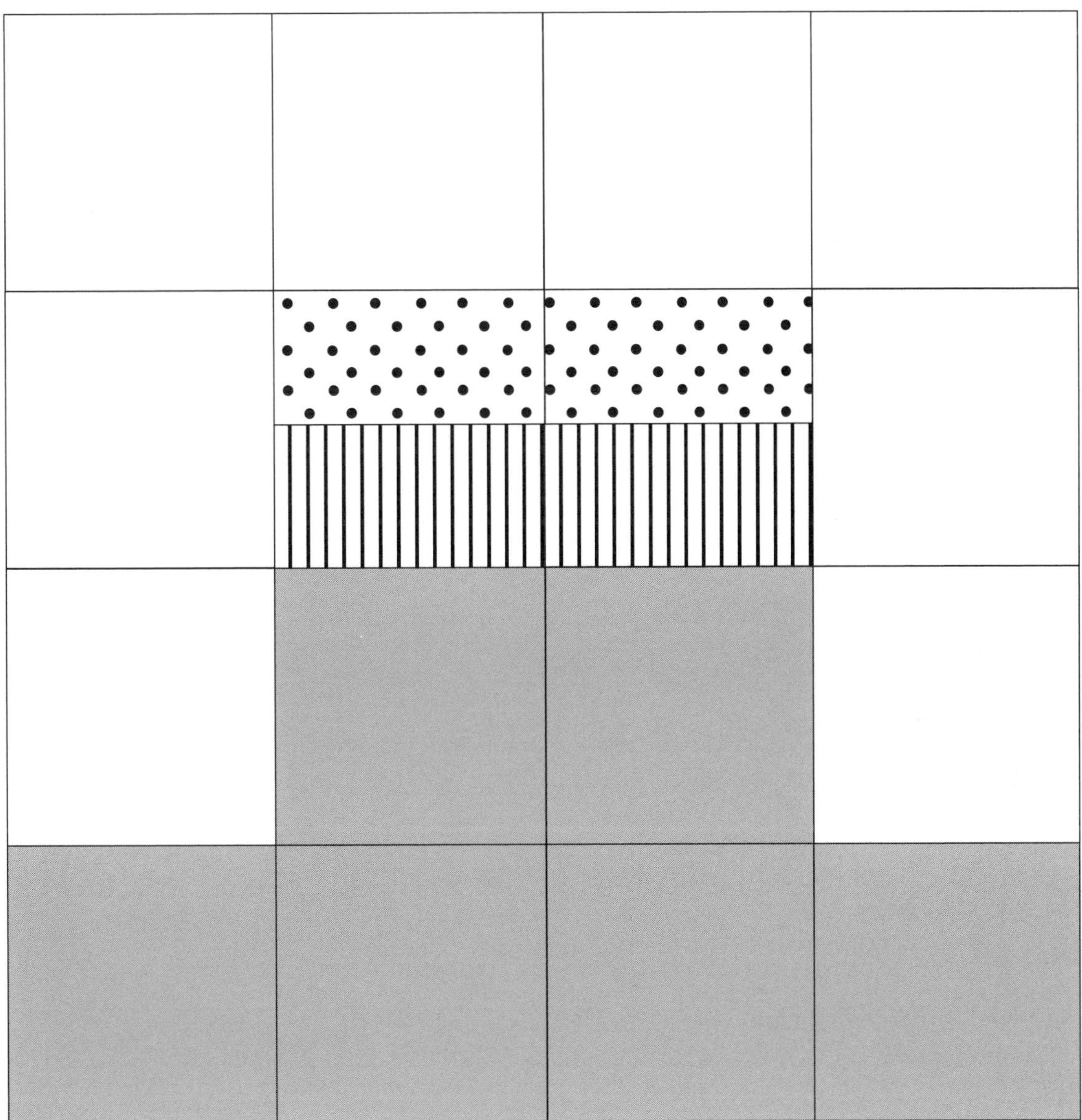

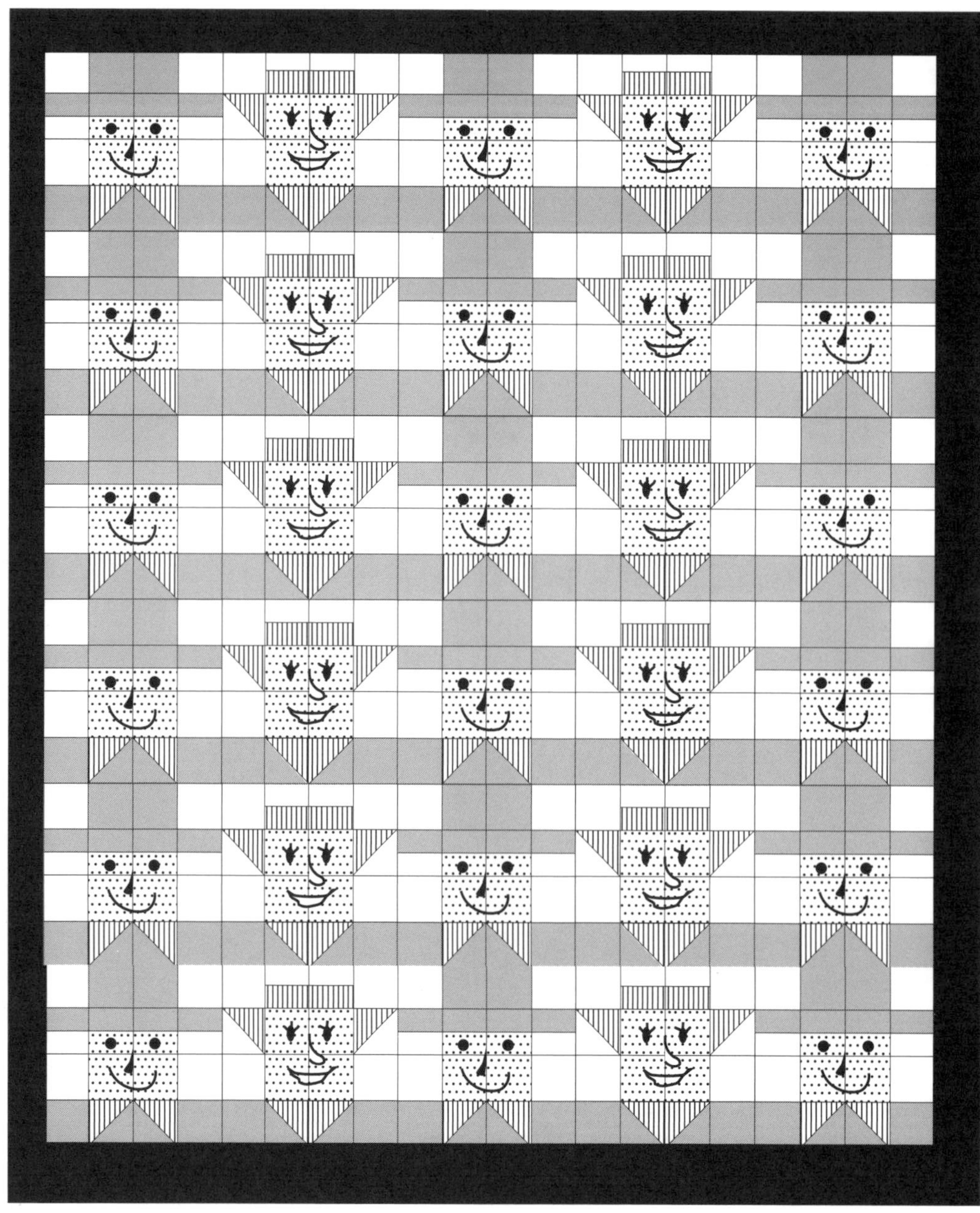

Note: Once the quilt design has been selected, you might need to make extra quilt blocks to complete a row.

Pilgrim Quilt

Lesson Synopsis

Materials Needed

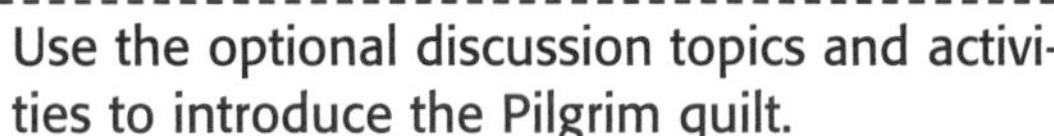

Use the optional discussion topics and activities to introduce the Pilgrim quilt.

For the introduction (optional)
- *Sarah Morton's Day: A Day in the Life of a Pilgrim Girl* by Kate Waters
- *Samuel Eaton's Day: A Day in the Life of a Pilgrim Boy* by Kate Waters
- For extensive information about the Pilgrims and the native peoples they encountered, write Plimoth Plantation, Inc., PO Box 1620, Plymouth, MA 02362, or call 1-800-262-9356.

The teacher and the class meet at the rug. The teacher introduces the Pilgrim man quilt block that will form half of the quilt. The children explore the ideas of area and one-half as they learn how to construct the block with the teacher's help. Then they go to the tables to construct their own Pilgrim man quilt blocks.

For the teacher and each child to make a Pilgrim man quilt block
- one Pilgrim man blackline, page 68
- three 1½″ square of peach construction paper
- one 1½″ square of white construction paper
- seven 1½″ squares of black construction paper
- five 1½″ squares of light blue construction paper
- scissors and glue
- crayons

The teacher and the class meet again at the rug. The teacher introduces the Pilgrim woman quilt block that will form the other half of the quilt. The children explore the ideas of area and one-half as they learn how to construct the block with the teacher's help. Then they go to the tables to make their own Pilgrim woman quilt blocks.

For the teacher and each child to make a Pilgrim woman quilt block
- one Pilgrim woman blackline, page 69
- four 1½″ square of peach construction paper
- three 1½″ squares of white construction paper
- three 1½″ squares of black construction paper
- six 1½″ squares of light blue construction paper
- scissors and glue
- crayons

When the glued blocks have dried, the children work in small groups to find good shapes and patterns for the quilt using tiles equal to the number of quilt blocks made by the class. They gather at the rug, share their solutions, and select their favorite as the model for assembling the quilt. The quilt is assembled and glued on bulletin board paper.

For the teacher and each small group
- 1″ square tiles of one color equal to the number of Pilgrim man quilt blocks
- 1″ square tiles of another color equal to the number of Pilgrim woman quilt blocks

To assemble the quilt
- all the dry Pilgrim man and woman quilt blocks
- one color cube per child
- one large sheet of light blue bulletin board paper
- glue

The quilt is displayed on the wall, and the children discuss patterns they see in it.

Curriculum Connections

Introducing the Quilt

Read and discuss *Sarah Morton's Day: A Day in the Life of a Pilgrim Girl* and *Samuel Eaton's Day: A Day in the Life of a Pilgrim Boy* by Kate Waters. Both books provide accurate accounts of the lives of young Pilgrims in early Massachusetts and contain photographs of the reconstructed village of Plimoth, children's clothing, and children's daily activities.

Modify the text as needed. Use the photographs to spark discussion. Ask the children questions: What was Sarah's house like? Samuel's house? How are they different from your house? Did they have their own bedrooms? Are their beds like yours? How did Sarah and Samuel dress? Did they dress differently from the way you dress? What did they eat? How did they get their food? Do you eat and get your food the same way? Do you have to work like they do? Do Sarah and Samuel go to school? What kinds of things are important for them to learn to do? Are they the same things you need to learn? How are Sarah and Samuel like you?

You might want to make corn bread from the simple recipe in *Sarah Morton's Day.*

Tell the children they are going to make a quilt showing Pilgrim men and women.

There are two ways to proceed with this quilt

option 1 - Each child can complete both quilt blocks, making a quilt of forty to sixty blocks.
option 2 - Half the students can complete the Pilgrim man blocks while the other half completes the Pilgrim woman blocks, making a quilt of twenty to thirty blocks.

Once you have decided how large a quilt your class will make, proceed with steps 1 and 2 and distribute the blacklines accordingly.

Making the Pilgrim Man Quilt Block

Overview

▼ Introduce the Pilgrim man blackline.
▼ Children learn how to construct a Pilgrim man quilt block.
▼ Children make their own Pilgrim man quilt blocks.

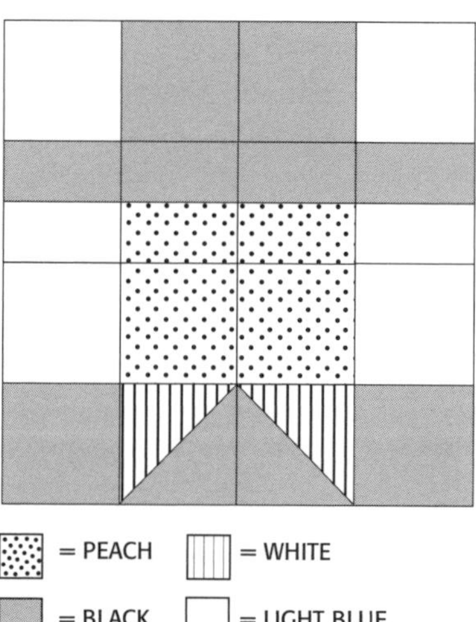

Have the 1½″ paper squares, scissors and blacklines on hand.

Gather the children at the rug. Give each a Pilgrim man blackline. Have the children describe what they see.

Melissa: *There are four different colors of squares.*
Ronald: *It looks like a man with a hat.*
Rachel: *I see rectangles, triangles, and squares.*
Tony: *There are lots of dark squares.*

Display white, peach, black, and light blue squares. Ask the children where they think the different colors should be placed.

Teacher: *Where do you think these black and white squares will go?*
Jesse: *I think they cover the gray squares to make the clothes and hat on the man.*
Thomas: *The white squares can make the collar.*
Teacher: *What about these peach squares?*
Karin: *They should go on the face, over the dots.*
Teacher: *All we have left are the light blue squares.*
Micheleen: *They probably cover the white part for the sky.*

Explore the ideas that a square is made up of two triangles and that each triangle is half of the square. See Triangles and Halves, page 10, for this discussion.

Explain that you have only squares, no triangles or rectangles, with which to cover the quilt block. Challenge the children to find a way to make rectangles and triangles from the squares.

Hold up a black square. Ask how many black squares are needed to cover the Pilgrim man's hat and jacket. Have volunteers explain their reasoning. Count out the number of squares suggested and test their predictions.

Repeat the procedure with the white and peach squares.

Explain that the light blue squares will be used for the sky around the Pilgrim man, and they will cover the white area. Have the children figure out how many light blue squares they will need and test their predictions.

Explore area as you help the children compute the number of squares of each color needed to cover the quilt block. See Early Experiences in Area, page 12, for this discussion.

Place all the paper squares (one color at a time) and scissors at the tables. Have the children go to their tables to cut and place the squares correctly onto the pilgrim man blacklines. Once they have placed the first color, put out the second color, and so on.

DON'T put glue on the tables until everyone has placed his or her pieces correctly.

Then distribute glue to the tables. When the children have finished gluing all the squares, triangles and rectangles in place, have them cut out their quilt blocks carefully around the edges so no white remains. Put the blocks aside to dry.

Step 2

Making the Pilgrim Woman Quilt Block

Overview

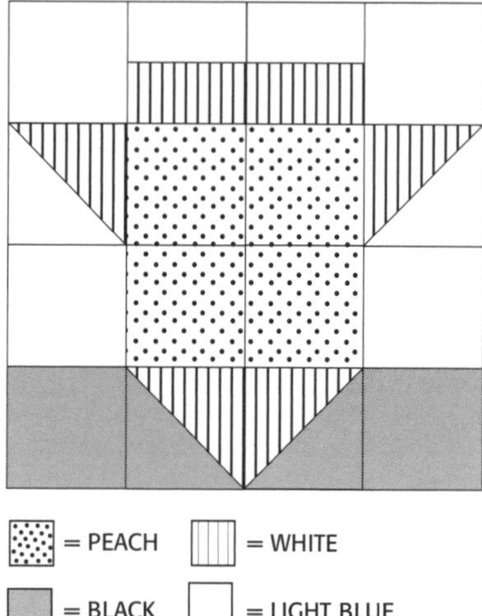

▼ Introduce the Pilgrim woman blackline.
▼ Children learn how to construct a Pilgrim woman quilt block.
▼ Children make their own Pilgrim woman quilt blocks.

Have the 1½″paper squares, scissors and blacklines on hand.

Gather the children at the rug. Give each a Pilgrim woman blackline. Have volunteers describe what they see.

Rachel: *I see rectangles, triangles, and squares.*

Display the white, peach, black, and light blue squares. Ask the children where they think the different colors should be placed.

Teacher: *Where do you think these black squares will go?*
Joe: *I think they cover the gray squares to make the dress.*
Teacher: *What about these peach squares?*
Kevin: *I think they cover the dots to make the face.*
Tim: *The white squares must cover the lines to make the collar and hat.*
Michele: *The blue squares must cover the white part for the sky.*

Hold up a peach square. Ask how many peach squares are needed to cover the Pilgrim woman's face, and have volunteers explain their reasoning.

Explain that you have only squares, no triangles or rectangles, with which to cover the Pilgrim woman's clothing. Challenge them to find a way to make rectangles and triangles from the squares.

Have them figure out the number of white squares needed for the collar and hat. Count out the number of squares suggested and test their predictions. Repeat the procedure with the black squares to cover the dress.

Finally, have the children figure out the number of light blue squares needed for the background and test their predictions.

Place all the squares (one color at a time) and scissors at the tables. Have the children go to their tables to cut and place the squares correctly onto the Pilgrim woman blacklines. Once they have placed the first color, put out the second color, and so on.

DON'T put glue on the tables until everyone has placed his or her pieces correctly.

Then distribute glue to the tables. When the children have finished gluing all the squares, triangles and rectangles in place, have them cut out their quilt blocks carefully around the edges so no white remains. Put the blocks aside to dry.

Distribute the dried Pilgrim man and woman quilt blocks and crayons to the children. Ask what is missing from the Pilgrims' faces (eyes, mouths, etc.). Have the children draw the facial features on their Pilgrim quilt blocks.

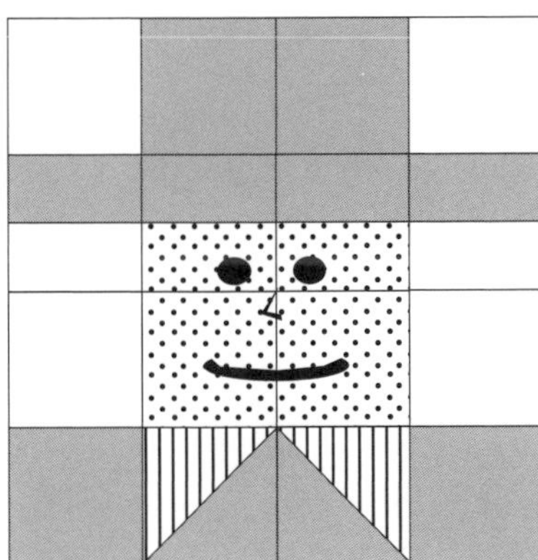

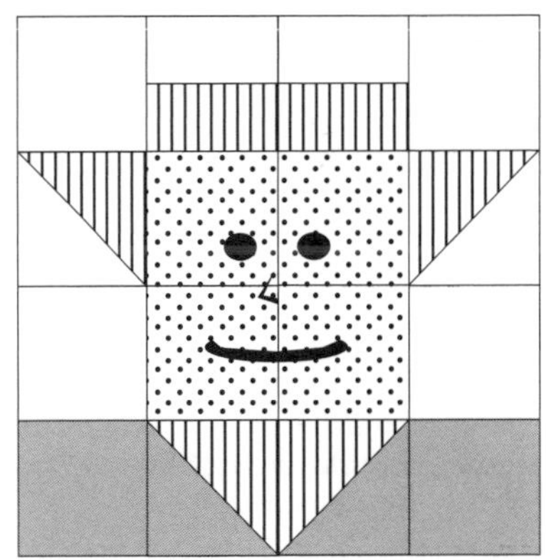

Step 3

Assembling the Quilt

Explore shape and size. See Computing the Size of the Quilt, page 17, for this discussion.

Gather the children at the rug and tell them that they will use tiles to decide on a good size, shape and pattern for the quilt. Divide them into small groups of two to four. Give each group a set of tiles equal to the number of quilt blocks that have been made by the class. Half of each set should be in one color, half in the other, to represent the two kinds of quilt blocks.

Have the groups experiment with the tiles to find a good size and shape for the quilt. (Don't worry about pattern at this point.) Here are some example for twenty-six blocks:

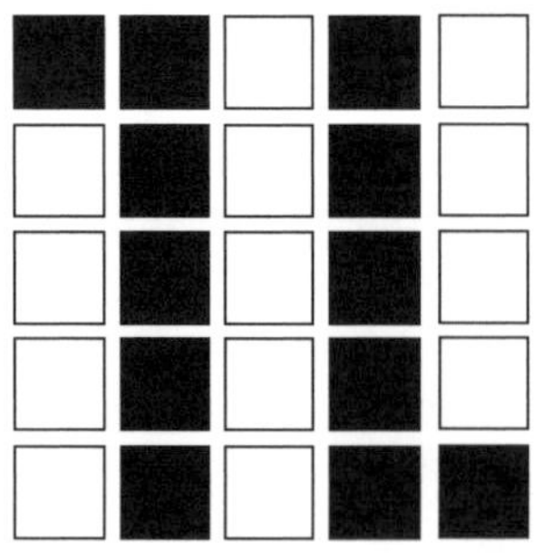

5 x 5 square with one block left over

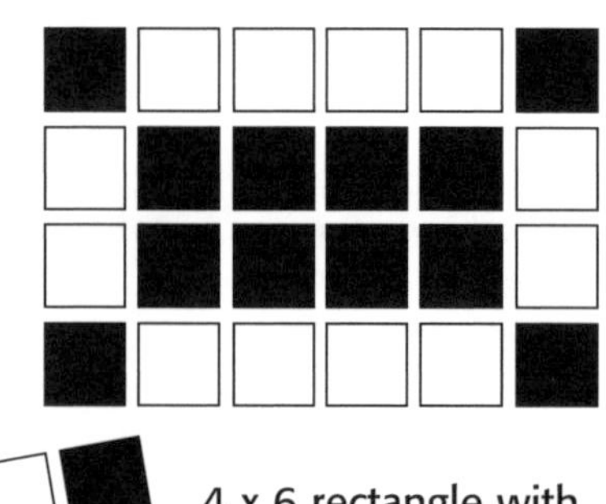

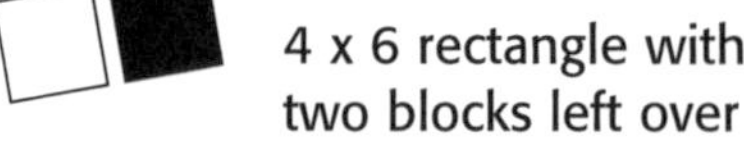

4 x 6 rectangle with two blocks left over

Ask each group to share its favorite shape. Choose one of the shapes for the class's quilt.

Next ask all the groups to arrange their tiles in the selected shape and experiment to find a good pattern for the tiles. As the children come up with ideas, let them use the quilt blocks to test their plans. Some patterns look better with the quilt blocks than with the tiles.

Explore counting in multiples while assembling the quilt. See Counting (and Counting in Multiples), page 21, for this discussion.

Ask each group to arrange its favorite design in the center of the rug. Give each child a color cube. Explain that each person may cast one vote for his or her favorite design by placing a color cube on that design.

See Making Quilt Block Pillows, page 20, for how to turn leftover quilt blocks into a mini art project.

Arrange the quilt blocks in the selected pattern, counting aloud until all the blocks have been placed. Glue the blocks on the bulletin board paper, leaving a border.

If you have leftover quilt blocks, they can be made into pillows.

Searching for Patterns and Designs

See Hidden Patterns and Designs, page 22, for a complete discussion of exploring patterns in finished quilts.

Hang the quilt on the wall for all to admire. Encourage the children to find designs and patterns hidden in the quilt. You may choose to record their comments on paper idea bubbles and attach them to the quilt.

The Pilgrim men are all in lines going down the quilt.

Now the Pilgrim men's hats are pointed on the top.

The hats go black, white, black, white.

Pilgrim Man

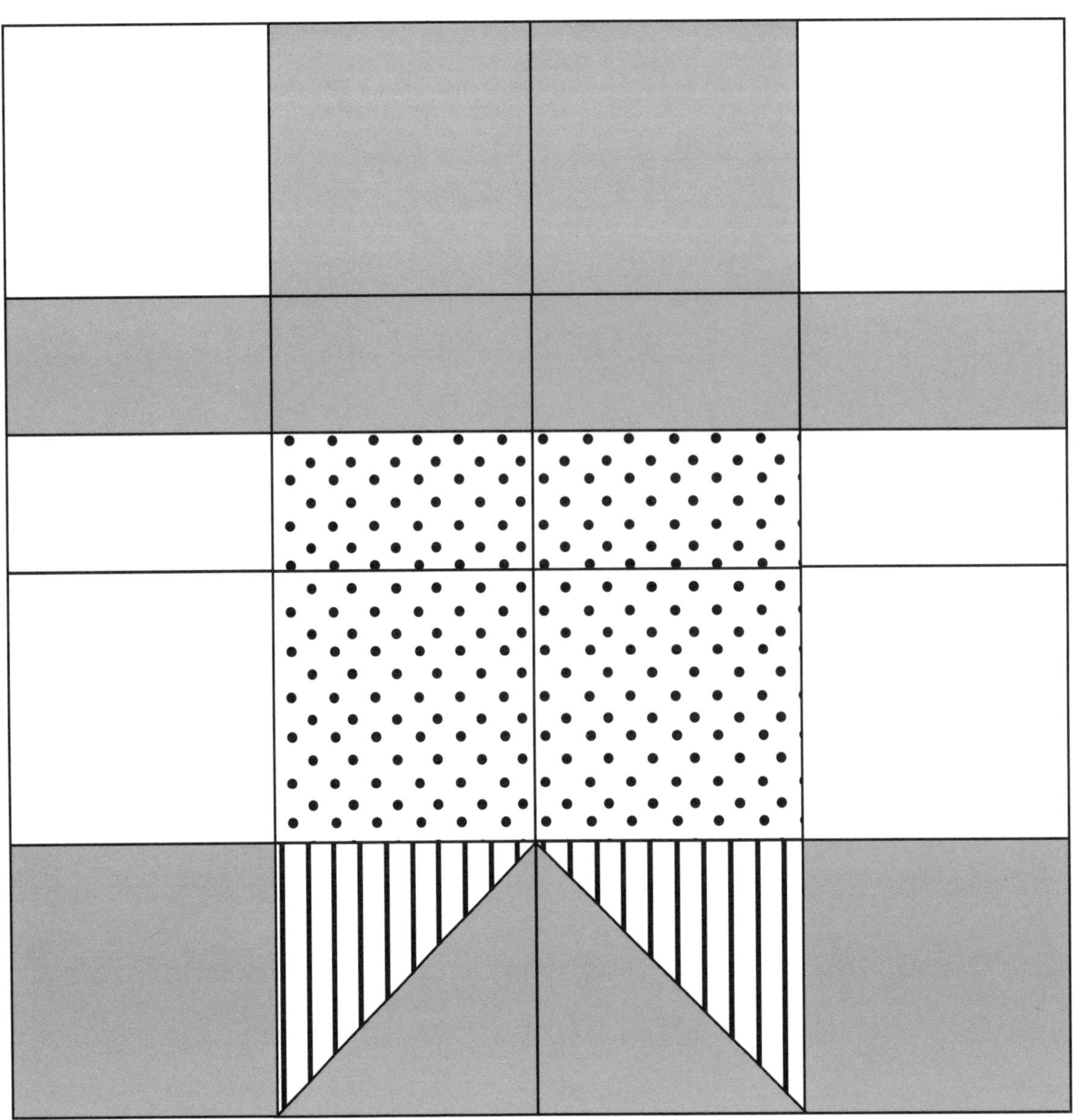

Pilgrim Woman

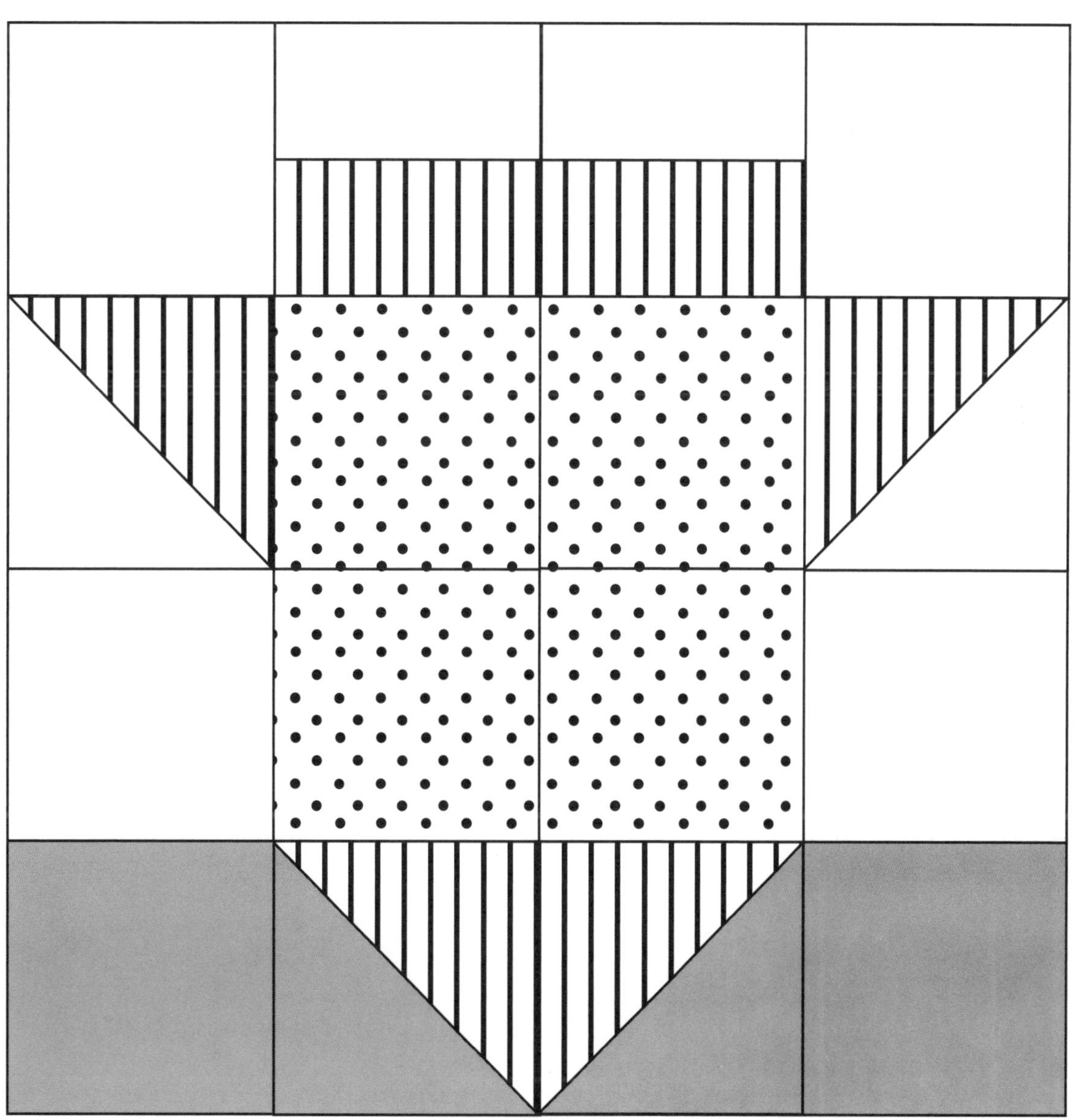

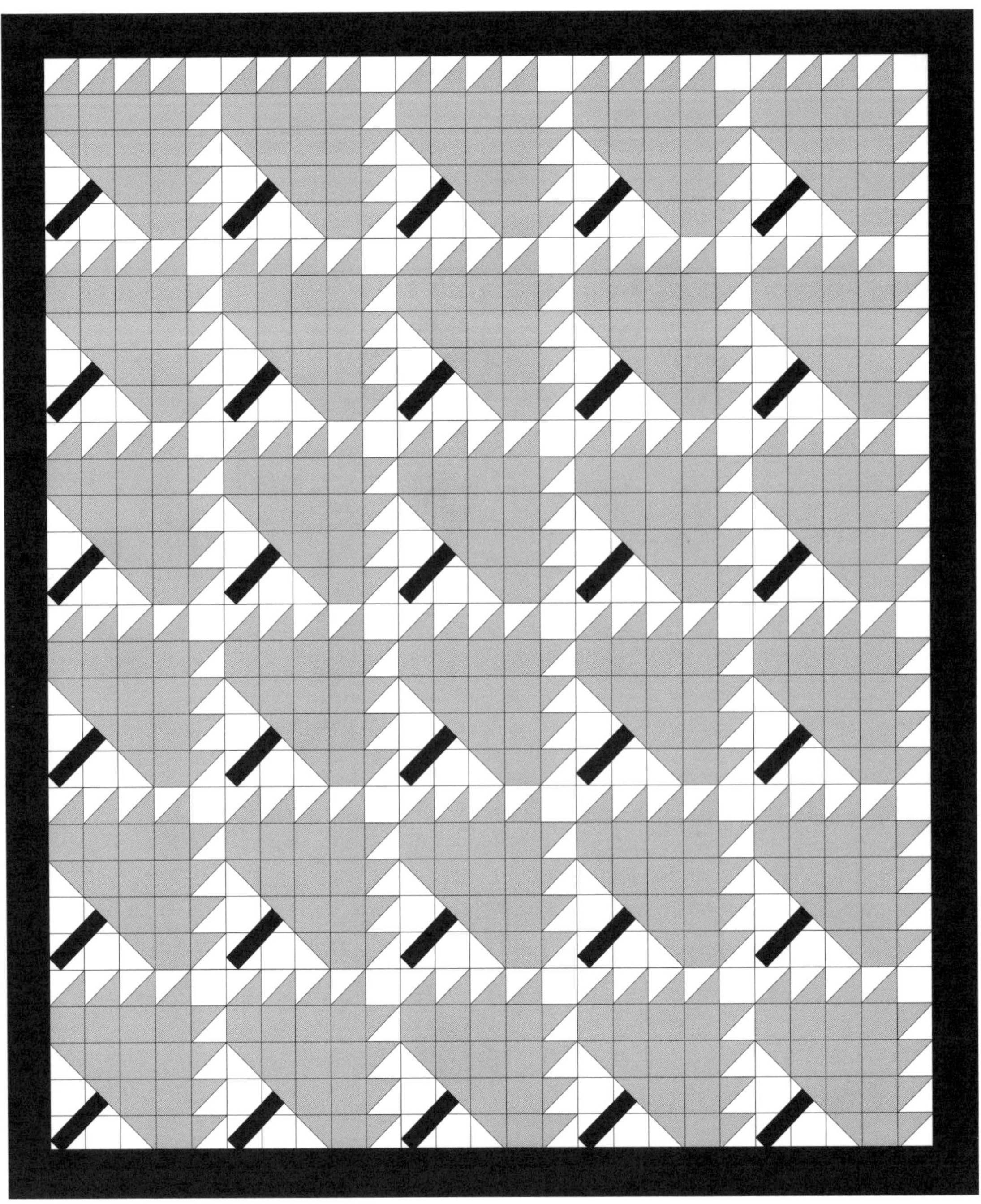

Note: This quilt is assembled from four-block squares. You will need a number of quilt blocks that is divisible by eight (16, 24, 32, etc.). You might need to make extra blocks.

Pine Tree Quilt

	Lesson Synopsis	Materials Needed
 Curriculum Connections	Use the optional discussion topics and activities to introduce the pine tree quilt.	**For the introduction (optional)** • *The Seasons Sewn* by Ann Whitford Paul • quilts brought from home
Step 1	The teacher and the class meet at the rug. The teacher introduces the pine tree quilt block that will form the quilt. The children explore the ideas of area and one-half as they learn how to construct the block with the teacher's help. Then they go to the tables to make their own pine tree quilt blocks.	**For the teacher and each child to make a pine tree quilt block** • one pine tree blackline, page 75 • sixteen 1″ squares of green construction paper • ten 1″ squares of blue construction paper • one 2¼″ x ½″ strip of brown construction paper • scissors and glue
Step 2	When the glued blocks have dried, the children work in small groups to find different patterns in a four-block quilt square. They gather at the rug, share their patterns, and select their favorite. The quilt is assembled from multiples of the selected square and glued on bulletin board paper.	**To assemble the quilt** • all the dry pine tree quilt blocks • one color cube per child • one large sheet of white bulletin board paper • glue
Step 3	The quilt is displayed on the wall, and the children discuss patterns they see in it.	

Introducing the Quilt

Read and discuss the winter chapter of *The Seasons Sewn*. Explain how some quilt blocks may have been invented and handed down to quilters today. Encourage the children to say which quilts they like and why.

Tell the children they are going to make a pine tree quilt.

Making the Pine Tree Quilt Block

Overview

▼ Introduce the pine tree blackline.
▼ Children learn how to construct a pine tree quilt block.
▼ Children make their own pine tree quilt blocks.

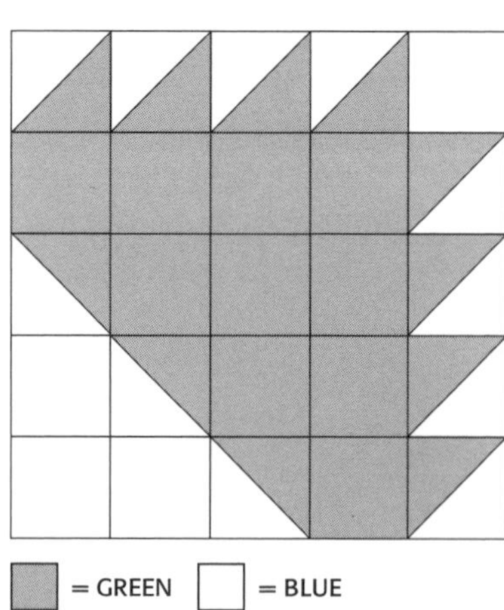

Have the 1″ paper squares, brown paper strip, scissors and blacklines on hand.

Gather the children at the rug. Give each a pine tree blackline. Have volunteers describe what they see.

Children: *There are triangles and squares. Some are white and some are gray. It looks a little like a Christmas tree turned on its side. Oh! Oh! I know. It's the pine tree quilt block! Yes, it's from the book we read yesterday.*

Explore the ideas that a square is made up of two triangles and that each triangle is half of the square. See Triangles and Halves, page 8, for this discussion.

Show the children your pine tree blackline and some green squares. Ask the children where they think the green squares go. Point to a shaded triangle in the pine tree. Explain that you have no triangles to cover it. Challenge them to find a way to make triangles from the square.

Explore area as you help the children compute the number of squares of each color needed to cover the quilt block. See Early Experiences in Area, page 12, for this discussion.

Ask the children to figure out how many green squares they will need to cover the pine tree. Have volunteers explain their reasoning. Count out the number of squares suggested and test their predictions.

Next, explain that the blue squares will cover the background to look like the sky. Have children figure out the number of blue squares needed and test their predictions.

Show the children a strip of brown paper and ask what part of the tree they think it will be (the trunk). Ask where they think it belongs.

Place the paper squares and scissors at the tables. Have the children go to their tables to cut and place the squares correctly onto the pine tree blacklines.

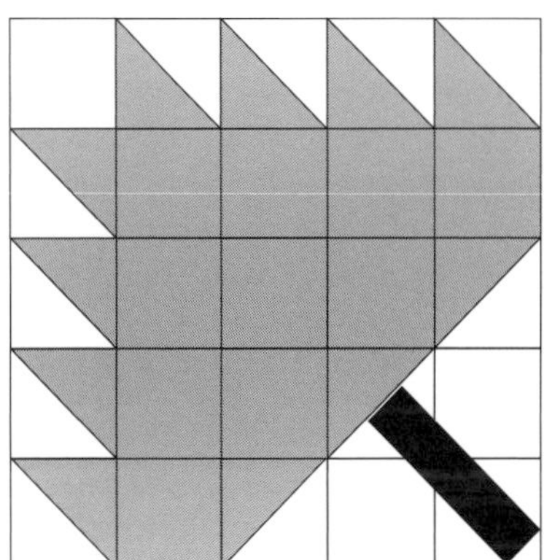

DON'T put glue on the tables until everyone has placed his or her pieces correctly.

Then distribute glue to the tables. When the children have finished gluing all the squares and triangles in place, have them glue on the brown paper trunks. Then the children should cut out their quilt blocks carefully around the edges so no white remains. Put the blocks aside to dry.

Assembling the Quilt

Gather the children at the rug. Lay out some of the real quilts they have brought to school. Have the children describe the shape of each of the quilts.

Children: *The little quilt is a square. The big quilts are all rectangles. I think the quilt on my wall at home is a square too. My big quilt is a rectangle. My bed is shaped like a rectangle so my quilt, I think, would be a rectangle too.*

Divide the children into groups of four. Give each group four pine tree quilt blocks. Show them how to place the four blocks together to make a four-block quilt square. Demonstrate rotating the blocks in different ways to create new designs.

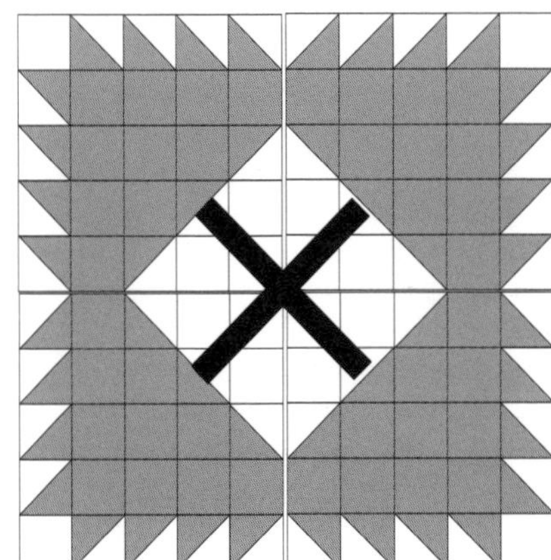

Help children discover patterns in the four-block quilt squares. See Slides and Rotations, page 14, for this discussion.

Encourage groups to experiment rotating the blocks to find a variety of designs. Allow time for the children to walk around and see other groups' designs.

Ask each group to arrange its favorite four-block design on the rug. Give each child a color cube. Explain that each person may cast one vote for his or her favorite design by placing a color cube on that design. Each group then builds the selected quilt square from its four blocks.

Arrange all the quilt squares together on the bulletin board paper to make the finished quilt. Glue the quilt on the bulletin board paper, leaving a border.

Searching for Patterns and Designs

Hang the quilt on the wall for all to admire. Encourage the children to find designs and patterns hidden in the quilt. You may choose to record their comments onto paper idea bubbles and attach them to the quilt.

See Hidden Patterns and Designs, page 22, for a complete discussion of exploring patterns in finished quilts.

There is a big diamond in the middle of four trees.

The stems make X's.

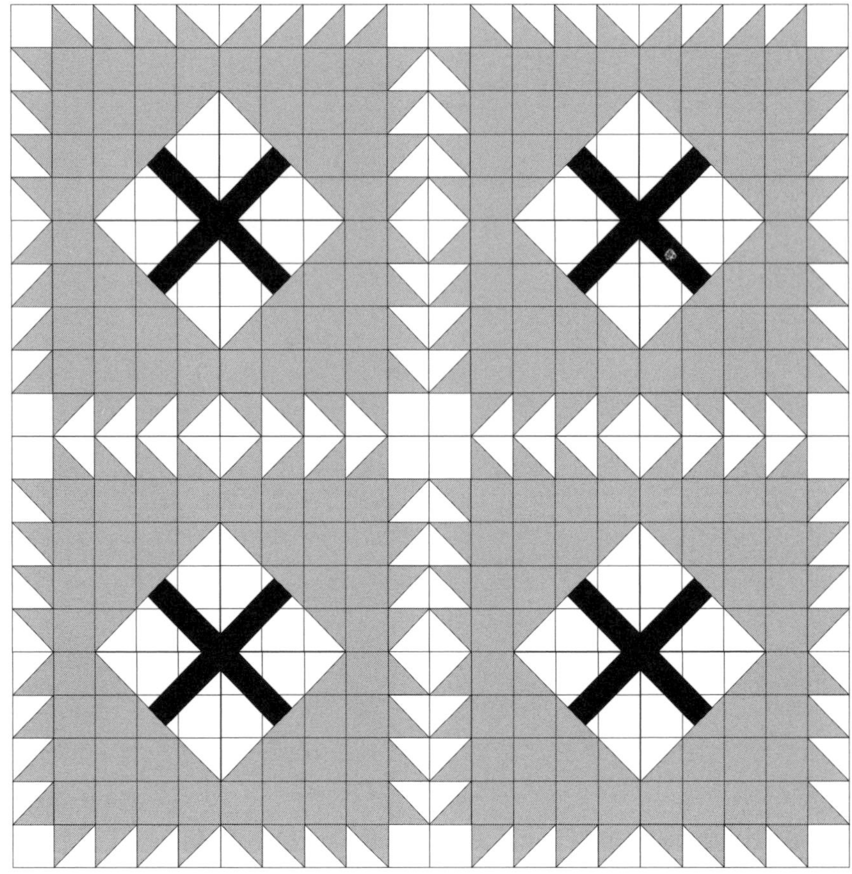

Pine Tree

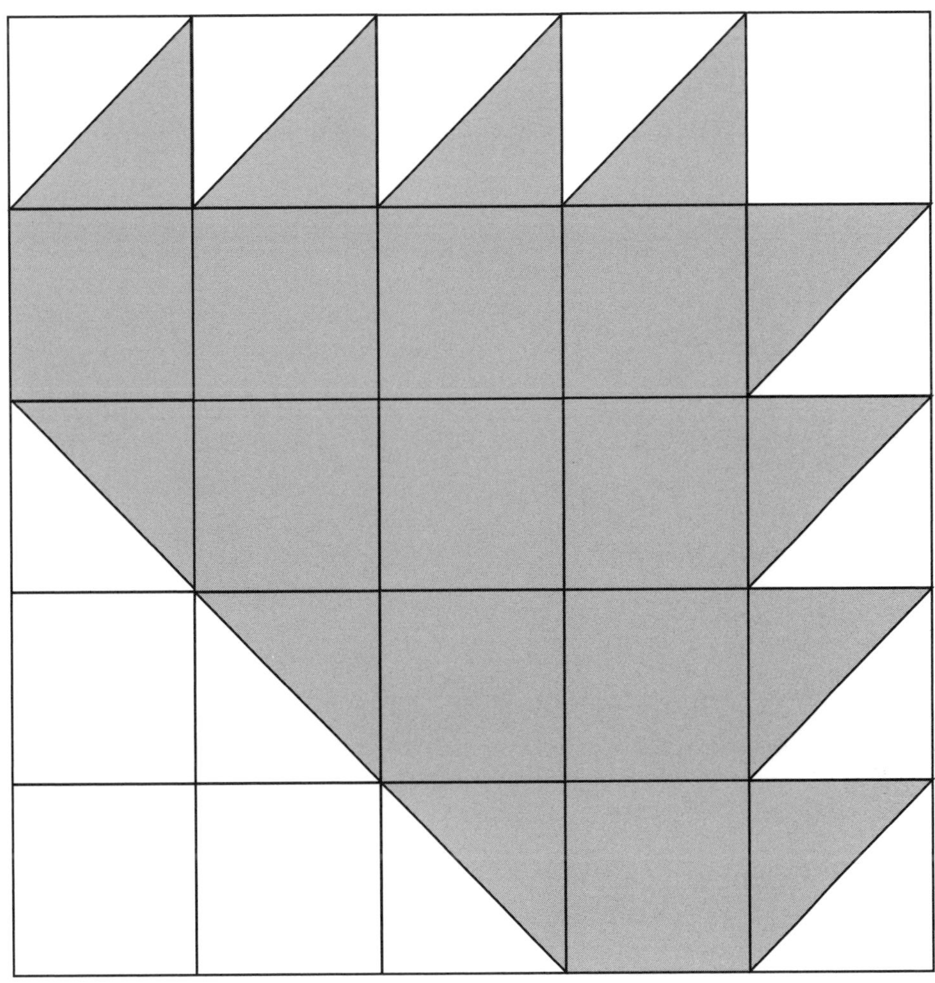

Polar Bear Quilt

24 BLOCK EXAMPLE

Note: Once you have determined the size of your quilt, you might need to make extra blocks to complete the checkerboard pattern.

Polar Bear Quilt

Curriculum Connections

Lesson Synopsis

Use the optional discussion topics and activities to introduce the polar bear quilt.

Materials Needed

For the introduction (optional)
- *A Polar Bear Journey* by Debbie Miller
- *The Christmas Wreath* by James Hoffman
- *"I Remember," Cried Grandma Pinky* by Jan Wahl
- *Selina and The Bear Paw Quilt* by Barbara Smucker
- nature videos about polar bears and their habitat

Step 1

The teacher and the class meet at the rug. The teacher introduces the polar bear quilt block that will form half of the quilt. The children learn how to construct a polar bear face with the teacher's help. Then they go to the tables to make their own polar bear quilt blocks.

For the teacher and each child to make a polar bear quilt block
- one 7″ square of light blue construction paper
- one 9″ x 12″ sheet of white construction paper
- crayons
- scissors and glue

Step 2

The teacher and the class meet again at the rug. The teacher introduces the bear paw quilt block that will form the other half of the quilt. The children explore the ideas of area and one-half as they learn how to construct the block with the teacher's help. Then they go to the tables to make their own bear paw quilt blocks.

For the teacher and each child to make a bear paw quilt block
- one bear paw blackline, page 83
- sixteen 1″ squares of white construction paper
- nine 1″ squares of red construction paper
- twenty-four 1″ squares of light blue construction paper
- scissors and glue

Step 3

When the glued blocks have dried, the children work with the teacher to create a checkerboard pattern. The quilt is glued on bulletin board paper.

To assemble the quilt
- all the dry polar bear and bear paw quilt blocks
- one large sheet of light blue bulletin board paper
- glue

Step 4

The quilt is displayed on the wall, and the children discuss patterns they see in it.

Introducing the Quilt

Gather the children at the rug. Ask them what they know about polar bears. Record their statements on chart paper. Read and discuss the nonfiction book *A Polar Bear Journey* by Debbie Miller. Or read these fiction books about polar bears: *The Christmas Wreath* by James Hoffman and *"I Remember," Cried Grandma Pinky* by Jan Wahl.

If you live near a zoo, you can go on a field trip or invite a zoo spokesperson to your class to talk about polar bears. You could also view polar bear videos from a library or video store.

After studying polar bears with your class, read *Selina and the Bear Paw Quilt* by Barbara Smucker. Explain that the story is about a real family that had to run away from a war and leave behind people they loved. Talk about how quilts can tie us to our past by helping us remember.

Tell the children they are going to make a polar bear quilt showing polar bear paws and faces.

Making the Polar Bear Face Quilt Block

Overview

▼ Children learn how to construct a polar bear face quilt block.
▼ Children make their own polar bear face quilt blocks.

Have the 7″ paper squares, 9″ x 12″ paper sheets, scissors and crayons on hand.

Gather the children at the rug. Tell them that they are going to make polar bear faces to go on the quilt.

Display a light blue square. Tell the children that this will be the background. Then show them a sheet of white paper. Tell them you will show them an easy way to make a polar bear head.

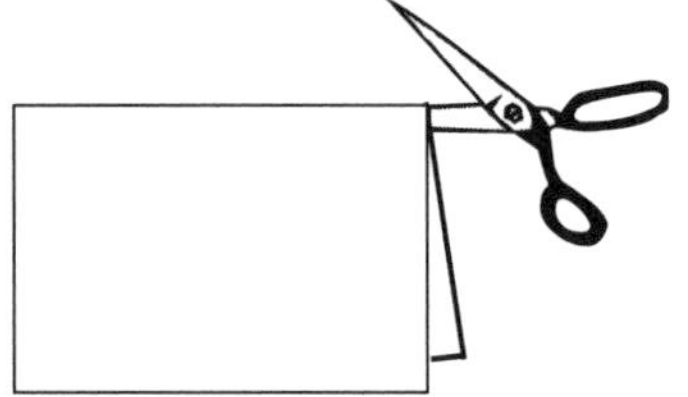

Fold the white construction paper in half lengthwise and cut along the fold line.

Take one half of the paper and draw a large circle that touches the edges on the two longer sides of the rectangle. Cut out the circle.

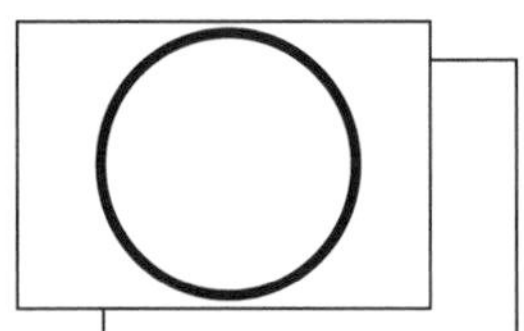

Next, fold the second half of the paper in half again lengthwise. Draw a circle that fills most of the space. Cut circles from both halves, following the pattern.

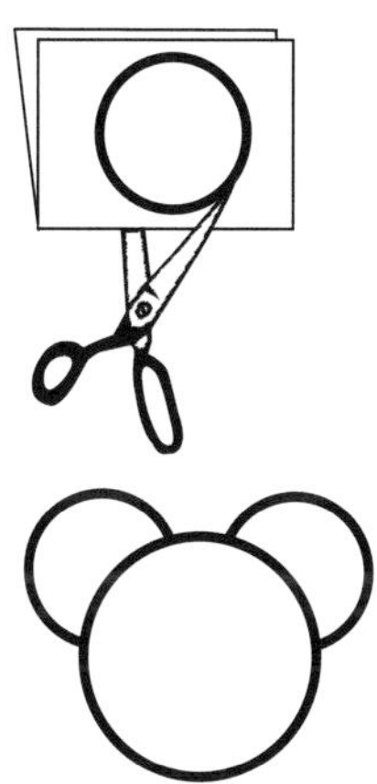

Slide the two smaller circles partway behind the large circle at the top. Ask the children what the two smaller circles form (the bear's ears). Glue the ears in place.

Draw in the bear's face with crayon. As you draw, elicit suggestions from the children about what to add. Then glue the finished polar bear face to the center of the light blue square.

Place the white sheets, light blue squares, scissors, glue and crayons at the tables. Have the children go to the tables to make their polar bear face quilt blocks. Put the blocks aside to dry.

Making the Bear Paw Quilt Block

Overview

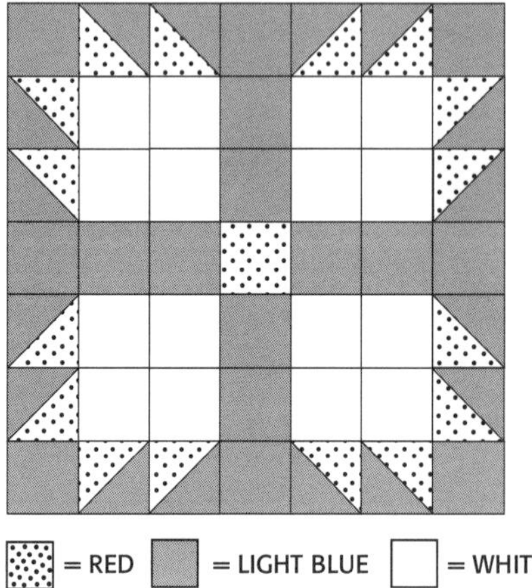

▼ Introduce the bear paw blackline.
▼ Children learn how to construct a bear paw quilt block.
▼ Children make their own bear paw quilt blocks.

Have the 1″ paper squares, scissors and blacklines on hand.

Gather the children at the rug. Give each a bear paw blackline. Have volunteers describe what they see.

Children: *There is a plus sign in the middle. I see four paws. There are sixteen triangles with dots and only one square with dots. There are sixteen gray squares, and sixteen white squares. There are also gray triangles.*

Display the white, red and light blue squares. Ask the children where they think the different colors should be placed.

Juan Carlo: *Polar bears have white feet, so I think the white will cover the big white squares.*
Micheleen: *I think the pointy claws will be red.*
Rachel: *Then the blue must be for the sky behind the paws.*

Explore the ideas that a square is made up of two triangles and that each triangle is half of the square. See Triangles and Halves, page 10, for this discussion.

Point to a dotted triangle on one of the bear paws. Explain that you have no red triangles to cover it. Show the children a red square, and challenge them to find a way to make triangles from the square.

Explore area as you help the children compute the number of squares of each color needed to cover the quilt block. See Early Experiences in Area, page 12, for this discussion.

Have the children figure out how many red squares they will need to cover all the dotted triangles and the dotted square. Have volunteers explain their reasoning. Count out the number of squares suggested and test their predictions.

Next, have children figure out the number of light blue squares needed for the background and test their predictions.

Repeat the procedure with the light blue squares.

DON'T put glue on the tables until everyone has placed his or her pieces correctly.

Place the paper squares and scissors at the tables. Have the children go to their tables to cut and place their squares correctly onto the bear paw blacklines.

Then distribute glue to the tables. When the children have finished gluing all the squares and triangles in place, have them cut out their quilt blocks carefully around the edges so no white remains. Put the blocks aside to dry.

Step 3

Assembling the Quilt

Gather the children at the rug. Have the polar bear face and bear paw quilt blocks in separate piles.

Tell the children you are going to make the quilt in a checkerboard pattern. Ask a volunteer to demonstrate what that looks like, or if no one knows, explain that the pattern could be bear paws, bear face, bear paws, bear face. Ask for a volunteer to show which block will come first.

Karin: *The bear paws will come first.* (She places a bear paw quilt block in the top left corner of the bulletin board paper.)
Teacher: *What comes next?*
Alipate: *The bear face will come next.* (He places a polar bear face block next to the bear paw block.)

Explore counting in multiples while assembling the quilt. See Counting (and Counting in Multiples), page 21, for this discussion.

Call on volunteers to place the rest of the blocks on the bulletin board paper in the correct order. Have the class chant the pattern and count the blocks as each one is placed. Make sure to have an odd number of blocks in each row to retain the checkerboard pattern. For example, if you have forty-eight blocks, a good quilt size would be a 5 x 9 rectangle with three blocks left over.

If you have leftover blocks, you can make them into pillows.

See Making Quilt Block Pillows, page 20, for how to turn leftover quilt blocks into a mini art project.

After all the quilt blocks have been arranged in a checkerboard pattern, glue them on the bulletin board paper, leaving a border.

Searching for Patterns and Designs

See Hidden Patterns and Designs, page 22, for a complete discussion of exploring patterns in finished quilts.

Hang the quilt on the wall for all to admire. Encourage the children to find designs and patterns hidden in the quilt. You may choose to record their comments onto paper idea bubbles and attach them to the quilt.

I see an AB pattern.

I see eight plus signs.

There are lots of red triangles and a few red squares.

Bear Paw

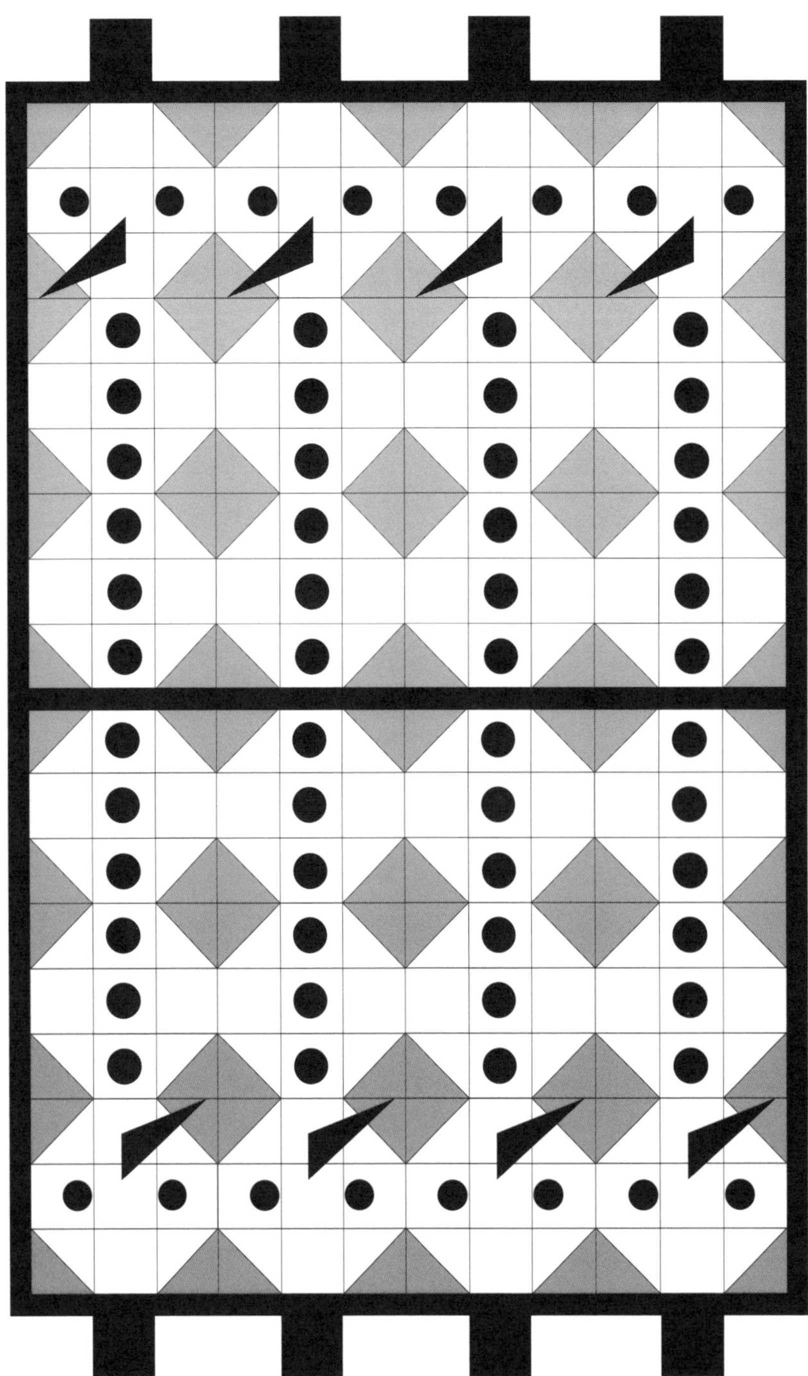

Note: Each snowman contains three snowball quilt blocks. You might need to make extra blocks to complete a snowman.

Snowman Quilt

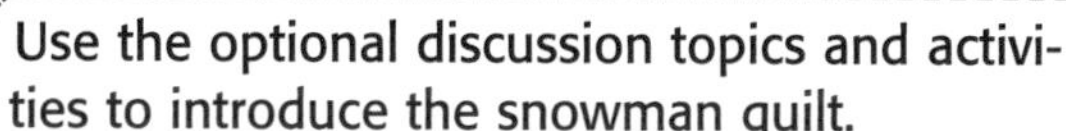

Lesson Synopsis

Materials Needed

Use the optional discussion topics and activities to introduce the snowman quilt.

For the introduction (optional)
- *Snowballs* by Lois Ehlert
- construction paper for snowman hats, mittens, scarves
- raisins or felt for eyes, mouth, and buttons
- baby carrots or felt for noses
- snow or white Styrofoam balls
- glue

The teacher and the class meet at the rug. The teacher introduces the snowball quilt block that will form the quilt. The children explore the ideas of area and one-half as they learn how to construct the block with the teacher's help. Then they go to the tables to make their own snowball quilt blocks.

For the teacher and each child to make a snowball quilt block
- one snowball blackline, page 89
- seven 2″ squares of white construction paper
- two 2″ squares of blue construction paper
- scissors and glue

When the glued blocks have dried, the children work in groups of three to assemble the top, bottom, and middle of their snowmen and glue them to pieces of newsprint.

For the teacher and each small group to make a snowman
- eight 1″ circles of black construction paper
- one 3″ long triangle of orange construction paper
- one 6″ x 18″ piece of newsprint

When the snowmen have dried, the children lay the snowmen in different arrangements, and select their favorite. The quilt is assembled and glued on bulletin board paper.

To assemble the quilt
- all the dry snowmen
- one large sheet of white bulletin board paper
- one 2″ x 3″ rectangle of black construction paper per snowman
- enough 2″ x 18″ strips of black construction paper to edge the quilt
- glue

The quilt is displayed on the wall, and the children discuss patterns they see in it.

Curriculum Connections

Introducing the Quilt

Read and discuss *Snowballs* by Lois Ehlert. Ask which children have made a snowball or a snowman. Have anyone who has made a snowman share what it was like. Discuss the number of snowballs it takes to make a snowman.

If you live in a snowy place, take your class out to make snowballs. Have the children build miniature snowmen with their snowballs. They can make hats and scarves and mittens out of construction paper and add them to their creations. Give them raisins for the eyes and mouths, and buttons or baby carrots for noses. Have them arrange the snowmen outside the classroom so the children can see them. The birds and other winter animals will enjoy the raisins and carrots.

For a math or science activity, you can have the children keep track of how long it takes for the snowmen to melt.

If you don't live where it snows, make snowmen from styrofoam.

Tell the children they are going to make a snowman quilt.

Making the Snowball Quilt Block

Overview

- ▼ Introduce the snowball blackline.
- ▼ Children learn how to construct the snowball quilt block.
- ▼ Children make their own snowball quilt blocks.

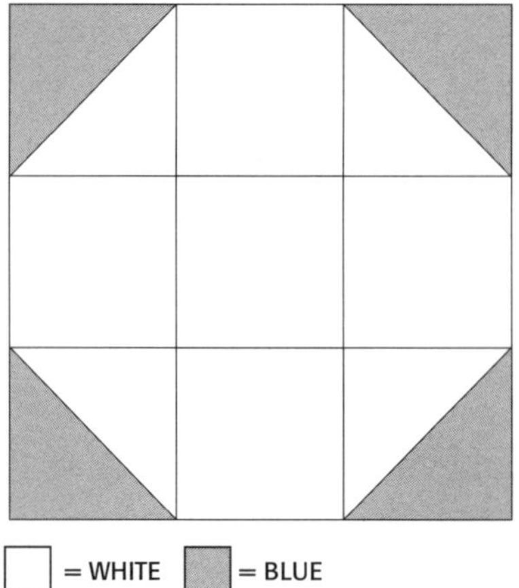

Have the 2″ paper squares, scissors and blacklines on hand.

Gather the children at the rug. Give each a snowball blackline. Have volunteers describe what they see.

Children: *There are triangles and squares. Some are white and some are gray. It looks like a funny ball.*

Show the children your snowball blackline and the white paper squares. Ask where they think the white squares will go.

Children: *They must go over the white part.*

Have children come up and place the white squares until no more can be placed.

Teacher: *All we have left in white is this shape.* (She points to a white triangle on the snowball blackline.)
Children: *Those are all triangles.*

Explore the ideas that a square is made up of two triangles and that each triangle is half of the square. See Triangles and Halves, page 8, for this discussion.

Explore area as you help the children compute the number of squares of each color needed to cover the quilt block. See Early Experiences in Area, page 12, for this discussion.

DON'T put glue on the tables until everyone has placed his or her pieces correctly.

Explain that you have no triangles to cover it. Show the children a white square. Challenge them to find a way to make triangles from the square.

Ask the children to figure out how many white squares they will need to cover the snowball, and have them explain their reasoning. Count out the number of squares suggested and test their predictions.

Next, explain that the blue squares will be used to cover the background. Have children figure out the number of blue squares needed and test their predictions.

Place the paper squares and scissors at the tables. Have the children go to their tables to cut and place their squares correctly onto the snowball blacklines.

Then distribute glue to the tables. When the children have finished gluing all the squares and triangles in place, they should cut out their quilt blocks carefully around the edges so no white remains. Put the blocks aside to dry.

Making the Snowmen

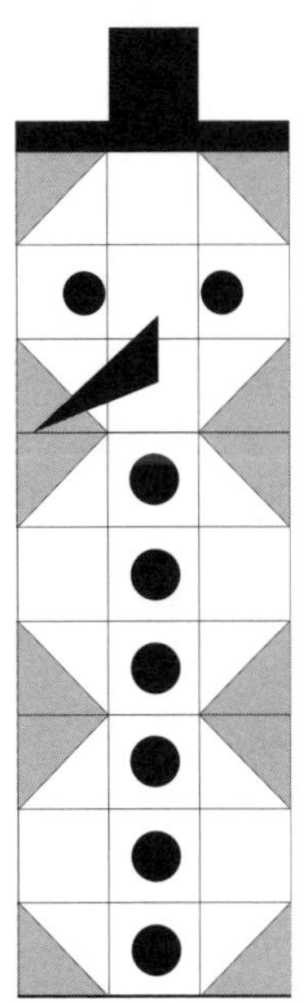

Overview

- ▼ Children learn how to construct a snowman from three snowball quilt blocks.
- ▼ Children work in groups to make snowmen.

Have three snowball quilt blocks, 1″ paper circles, 3″ paper triangles, and newsprint on hand.

Gather the children at the rug. Place the finished quilt blocks in the center of the rug. Tell the children they will use the snowballs to make snowmen for the quilt. Ask them how many snowballs are needed to make one snowman.

Children: *You need three snowballs: a head, a middle, and a bottom.*

Divide the children into groups of three and give each group three snowball quilt blocks. Have each group choose who will create which part of the snowman. Once they have decided, give each child whose block is to be the head two black paper circles for eyes and an orange paper triangle for the nose. Give each child whose block is to be the middle or bottom three black circles for paper buttons.

DON'T put glue on the tables until everyone has placed his or her pieces correctly.

Have them go to the tables and create their snowmen. When they have placed all their pieces, distribute glue and a piece of newsprint to each group. Have the children assemble the snowmen and glue them to the newsprint.

See Making Quilt Block Pillows, page 20, for how to turn leftover quilt blocks into a mini art project.

If you have extra snowball quilt blocks, you can make them into pillows.

Assembling the Quilt

Have groups bring their snowmen to the rug. Lay them side by side on the bulletin board paper. Have volunteers suggest different arrangements, then have the children vote for their favorite. Good arrangements can be made with six, eight, or ten snowmen, depending on your class size.

Glue the quilt on the bulletin board paper. Add the black paper edging and top hats. You can also add an additional strip of black paper to separate the rows of snowmen.

Searching for Patterns and Designs

See Hidden Patterns and Designs, page 22, for a complete discussion of exploring patterns in finished quilts.

Hang the quilt on the wall for all to admire. Encourage the children to find designs and patterns hidden in the quilt. You may choose to record their comments on paper idea bubbles and attach them to the quilt.

The black dots make four lines up and down the quilt.

All the triangle noses are pointing in the same direction.

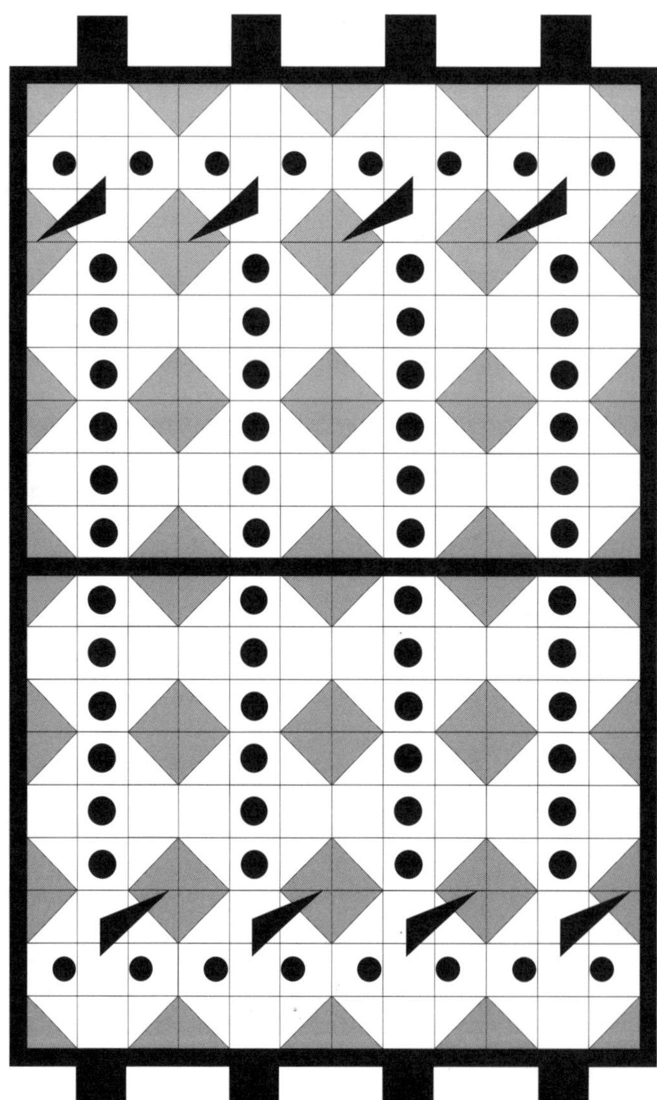

Snowball

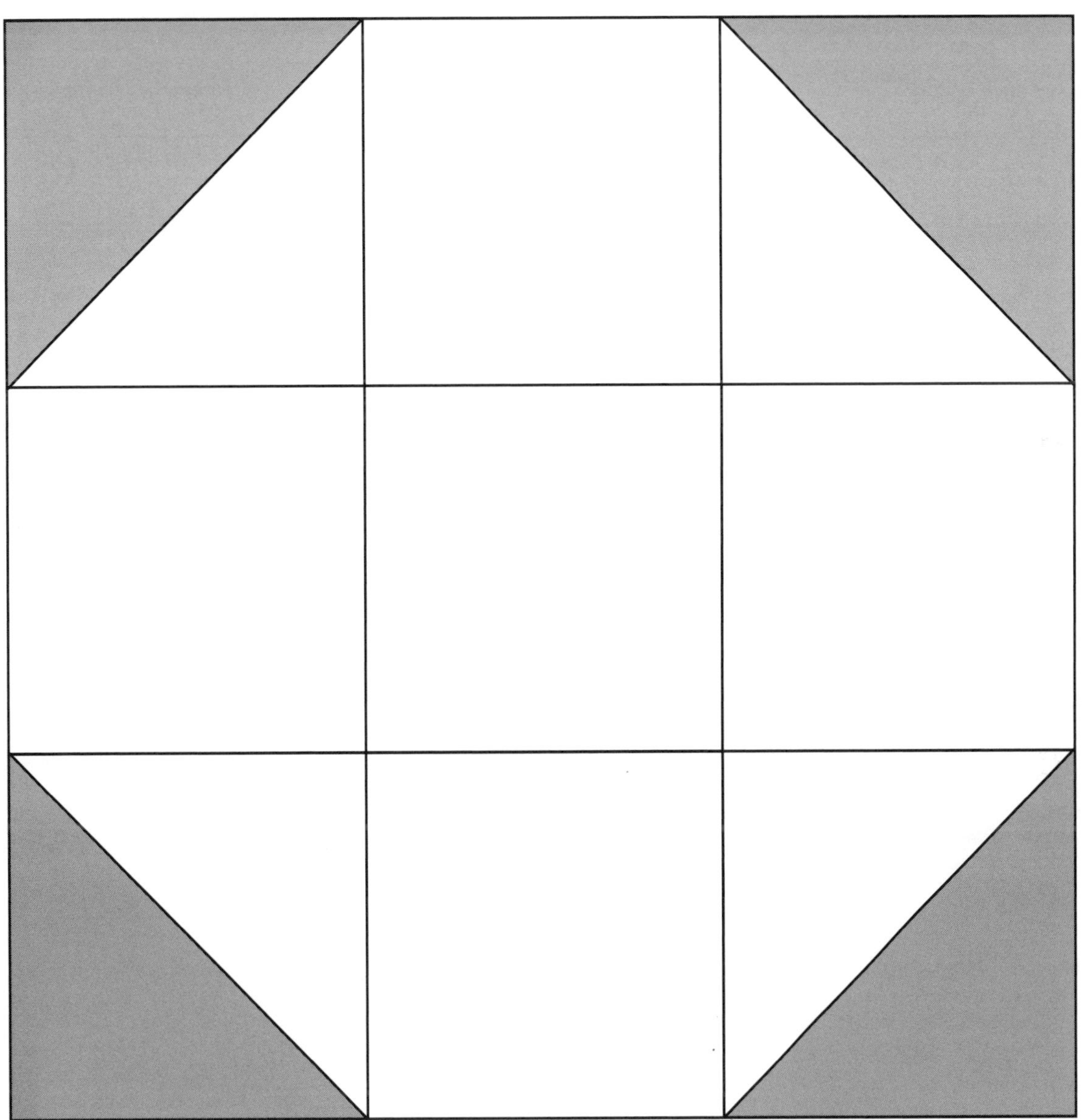

36 BLOCK EXAMPLE

Note: This quilt is assembled from four-block quilt squares. You will need a number of quilt blocks that is divisible by eight (16, 24, 32, etc.). You might need to make extra blocks.

River and Trees Quilt

Lesson Synopsis

Use the optional discussion topics and activities to introduce the river and trees quilt.

Step 1

The teacher and the class meet at the rug. The teacher introduces the river and trees quilt block that will form the quilt. The children explore the ideas of area and one-half as they learn how to construct the block with the teacher's help. Then they go to the tables to make their own river and trees quilt blocks.

Step 2

When the glued blocks have dried, the children work in small groups to find different patterns in a four-block quilt square. They gather at the rug, share their patterns, and select their favorite. The quilt is assembled from multiples of the selected square and glued on bulletin board paper.

The quilt is displayed on the wall, and the children discuss patterns they see in it.

Materials Needed

For the introduction (optional)

- *Sweet Clara and the Freedom Quilt* by Deborah Hopkinson

For the teacher and each child to make a river and trees quilt block

- one river and trees blackline, page 95
- five 1½″ squares of blue construction paper
- four 1½″ squares of dark green construction paper
- eight 1½″ squares of light green construction paper
- four 1½″ x ½″ strips of brown construction paper
- scissors and glue

To assemble the quilt

- all the dry river and trees quilt blocks
- one color cube per child
- one large sheet of green bulletin board paper
- glue

Introducing the Quilt

Read *Sweet Clara and the Freedom Quilt.* Ask why the characters in the story made freedom quilts. Point out that the story is based on real events in American history. Talk about slavery and the underground railroad. Discuss the part quilts played in helping slaves find their way to freedom.

Tell the children they are going to make a river and trees quilt to honor the enslaved African Americans, and those who escaped through the woods to freedom.

Making the River and Trees Quilt Block

Overview

- ▼ Introduce the river and trees blackline.
- ▼ Children learn how to construct the quilt block.
- ▼ Children construct their own river and trees quilt blocks.

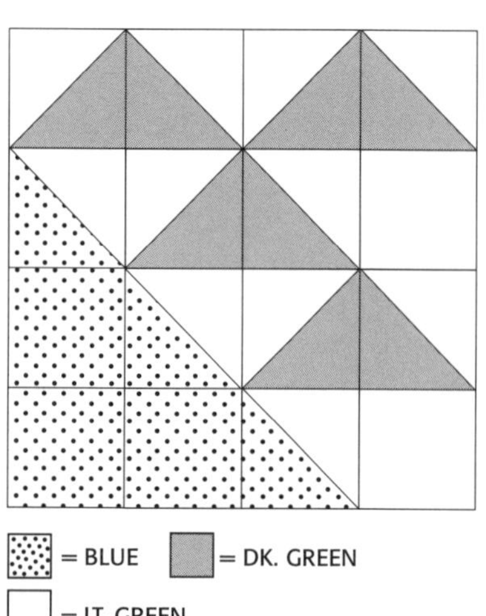

Have the $1\frac{1}{2}''$ paper squares, brown paper strip, scissors and blacklines on hand.

Gather the children at the rug. Give each a river and trees blackline. Have volunteers describe what they see.

Children: *There are triangles. The triangles are all touching. There are squares too.*

Explore the ideas that a square is made up of two triangles and that each triangle is half of the square. See Triangles and Halves, page 8, for this discussion.

Explore area as you help the children compute the number of squares of each color needed to cover the quilt block. See Early Experiences in Area, page 12, for this discussion.

Display blue, dark green, and light green squares. Remind the children this is a river and trees quilt block. Then ask where they think the different colors should go. (The blue covers the dotted part of the blackline to make the river. The dark green covers the shaded part to make trees. The light green covers the white part to make grass.)

Ask the children to figure out how many blue squares they will need to cover the river, and have volunteers explain their reasoning.

Teacher: *Do you all agree with Shamika that you need five squares to cover the river? I need some volunteers to come and prove it.*

(Sean places three blue squares over the three dotted squares. Shamika cuts two blue squares in half and places three of the triangles over the remaining triangles in the river.)

Shamika: *See. Five squares. It took five squares.*
Edward: *But you have a triangle left over.*
Shamika: *Yeah, but I had to cut a square to get one triangle. So I needed five squares altogether.*

Next, have the children figure out the number of dark green squares needed and test their predictions.

Follow the same procedure to place the light green squares.

Show the children a strip of brown paper and ask where it might belong. (It covers the black lines to make tree trunks.)

DON'T put glue on the tables until everyone has placed his or her pieces correctly.

Place the colored paper squares, brown strips, and scissors at the tables. Have the children go to their tables to cut and place their squares correctly onto the river and trees blacklines.

Then distribute glue to the tables. When the children have finished gluing all the squares and triangles in place, have them glue on the brown tree trunks. Then they should cut out their quilt blocks carefully around the edges so no white remains. Put the blocks aside to dry.

Assembling the Quilt

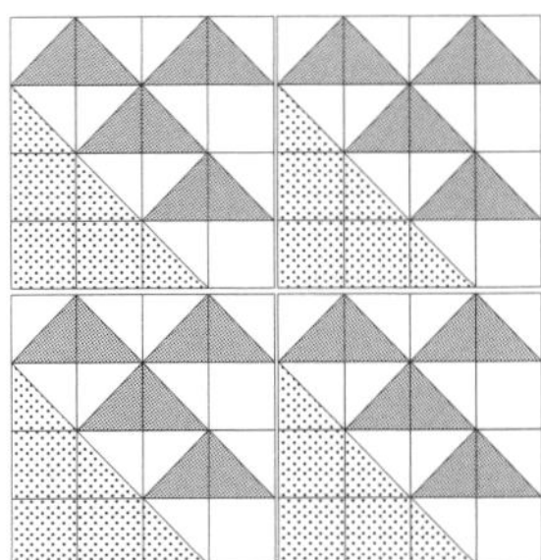

Group the children in fours and give each group four river and trees quilt blocks. Show them how to place the four blocks together to make a four-block quilt square. Demonstrate how new designs are created by rotating the blocks in different ways.

Help children discover patterns in the four-block quilt squares. See Slides and Rotations, page 14, for this discussion.

Encourage groups to experiment rotating the blocks to find a variety of designs. Allow time for the children to walk around and see other groups' designs.

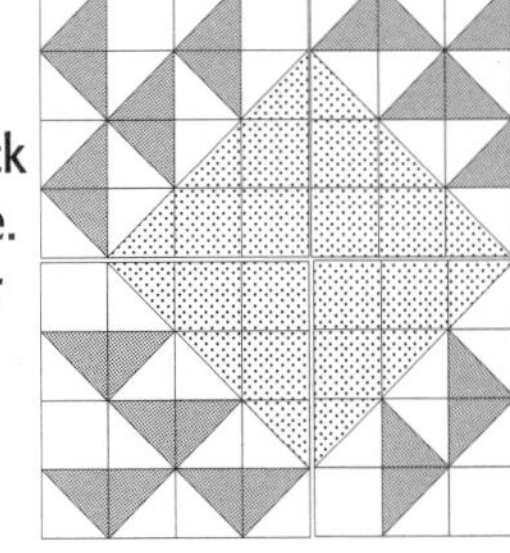

Ask each group to arrange its favorite four-block design on the rug. Give each child a color cube. Explain that each person may cast one vote for his or her favorite design by placing a color cube on that design. Then have each group build the selected quilt square from its four blocks.

See Making Quilt Block Pillows, page 20, for how to turn leftover quilt blocks into a mini art project.

If you have leftover blocks, you can make them into pillows.

Arrange all the quilt squares on the bulletin board paper to make the finished design. Glue them on the bulletin board paper, leaving a border.

Searching for Patterns and Designs

See Hidden Patterns and Designs, page 22, for a complete discussion of exploring patterns in finished quilts.

Hang the quilt on the wall for all to admire. Encourage the children to find designs and patterns hidden in the quilt. You may choose to record their comments on paper idea bubbles and attach them to the quilt. Note: The quilt below is not built from four-block quilt squares as described in the lesson; it illustrates another possible pattern that takes advantage of the block's unique design.

I see big blue diagonal stripes.

There are dark green triangles all over.

River and Trees

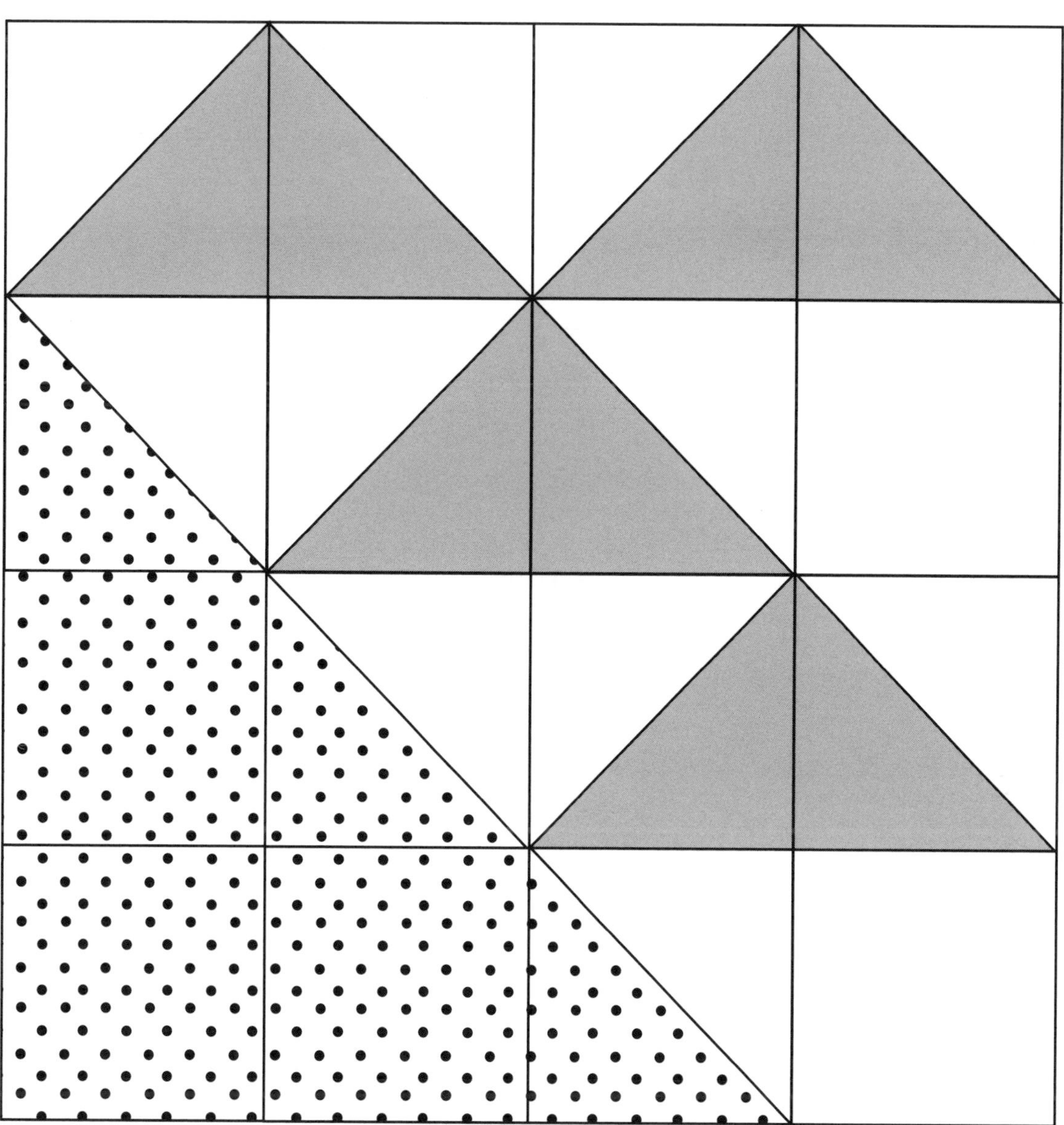

Note: Once you have determined the size of your quilt, you might need to make extra blocks to complete the checkerboard pattern.

Valentine Heart Quilt

Lesson Synopsis

Use the optional discussion topics and activities to introduce the valentine heart quilt.

The teacher and the class meet at the rug. The teacher introduces the heart quilt block that will form half of the quilt. The children explore the ideas of area and one-half as they learn how to construct a heart quilt block with the teacher's help. Then they go to the tables to make their own heart quilt blocks.

Step 2

The teacher and the class meet again at the rug. The teacher introduces the art supplies the children can use to make the decorated valentine quilt blocks that will form the other half of the quilt. The children choose their supplies and go to the tables to make their own decorated valentine quilt blocks.

Optional: The teacher sets up a store with the art supplies. The children buy supplies and use them to decorate their valentines.

Materials Needed

For the introduction (optional)

- *The Patchwork Quilt* by Valerie Flournoy

For the teacher and each child to make a heart quilt block

- one heart blackline, page 104
- eleven 1½″ squares of red construction paper
- five 1½″ squares of pink construction paper
- scissors and glue

For the teacher and each child to make a decorated valentine quilt block

- one 6″ square of pink construction paper folded in half with half a heart drawn on it, for cutting
- one 6″ square of red construction paper
- sequins
- glitter
- feathers
- bows
- scraps of fancy wrapping paper
- scraps of colored paper
- pom-poms
- scissors and glue

For the valentine store (optional)

- store plan blackline, page 105 (for each older child)
- art supplies (see above list)
- ten cents for each younger child (all pennies)
- fifteen cents for each older child (one nickel and one dime)
- money for making change
- price tags
- money cups for payment (one for each item)
- containers to hold goods for sale (shallow shirt boxes work well)
- small plastic bag for each child

When the glued blocks have dried, the children work with the teacher to create a checkerboard pattern. The quilt is glued on bulletin board paper.

To assemble the quilt
- all the dry heart and decorated valentine quilt blocks
- one color cube per child
- one large sheet of white or red bulletin board paper
- glue

The quilt is displayed on the wall, and the children discuss patterns they see in it.

Introducing the Quilt

Read and discuss *The Patchwork Quilt* by Valerie Flournoy. Ask why Grandma wanted to make a quilt instead of buying a new one. Talk about why Grandma said that a quilt doesn't forget. Ask what Tanya meant when she said that the quilt and Grandma were telling each other stories. Talk about the love that goes into making a quilt.

Remind the children that Valentine's Day is in February and discuss how Valentine's Day celebrates love. Tell the children they are going to make a handmade quilt filled with love just like Tanya and her family did in the story.

Step 1

Making the Heart Quilt Block

Overview

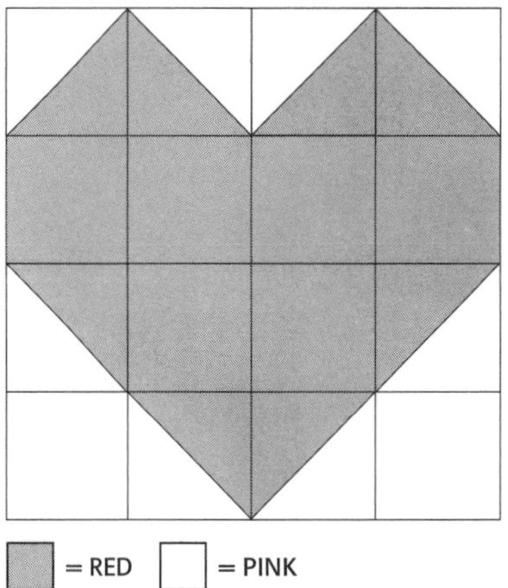

- ▼ Introduce the heart blackline.
- ▼ Children learn how to construct the heart quilt block.
- ▼ Children make their own heart quilt blocks.

Have the 1½″ paper squares, scissors and blacklines on hand.

Gather the children at the rug. Give each a heart blackline. Have volunteers describe what they see.

Children: *It looks like a heart made of squares and triangles.*

Ask what is different about its shape from other hearts they have seen. (It is more angular, not rounded.)

Display some of the small red and pink squares. Ask the children where they think the squares belong.

Explore the ideas that a square is made up of two triangles and that each triangle is half of the square. See Triangles and Halves, page 8, for this discussion.

Point to a shaded triangle on the heart blackline. Explain that you have no triangles to cover it. Show the children a red square. Challenge them to find a way to make triangles from the square.

Explore area as you help the children compute the number of squares of each color needed to cover the quilt block. See Early Experiences in Area, page 12, for this discussion.

Ask the children how many red squares are needed to cover the heart, and have them explain their reasoning. Count out the number of squares suggested and test their predictions.

Next, have children figure out the number of pink squares needed to cover the background and test their predictions.

Place the colored paper squares and scissors at the tables. Have the children go to their tables to cut and place their squares correctly onto the heart blacklines.

DON'T put glue on the tables until everyone has placed his or her pieces correctly.

Then distribute glue to the tables. When the children have finished gluing all the squares and triangles in place, have them cut out their quilt blocks carefully around the edges so no white remains. Put the blocks aside to dry.

Making the Decorated Valentine Block

Overview

▼ Introduce the decorated valentine block.
▼ Children learn how to cut out a paper heart and decorate it.
▼ Children construct their own decorated valentine quilt blocks.

Have the folded pink paper, scissors and art supplies on hand.

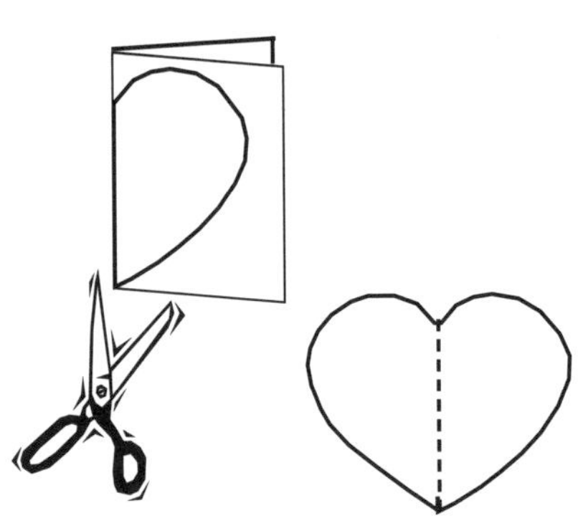

Gather the class at the rug. Explain that the children will make decorated valentine hearts to form the other half of the quilt. Show the children a piece of the folded pink paper with half a heart drawn on it. Ask a volunteer to cut along the line and then unfold the paper to make a complete heart.

Distribute the folded pieces of pink paper and scissors. Have the children go to the tables to cut out the hearts. Provide help as needed.

Meet again at the rug. Have the art supplies separated in shirt boxes or other shallow containers. Hand out plastic bags for the children to use to collect items for their valentines. You may choose to set up a "valentine store" where the children can select and purchase the supplies they need to decorate their valentines (see below). You might want to limit the amounts they can choose to ensure a fair distribution, and have the children come up in pairs.

Visiting the Valentine Store (optional)

Tell the children they will shop for art supplies to decorate their valentine hearts. Place a couple of the store items in containers labeled with the prices, along with pay cards and money cups in the center of the circle. Each pay card should show a labeled picture of the item, the price and coin stamps representing the price. It should be laid in front of the item so the children can match the price one-to-one before placing their coins in the cup. Each item is paid for separately and has its own money cup.

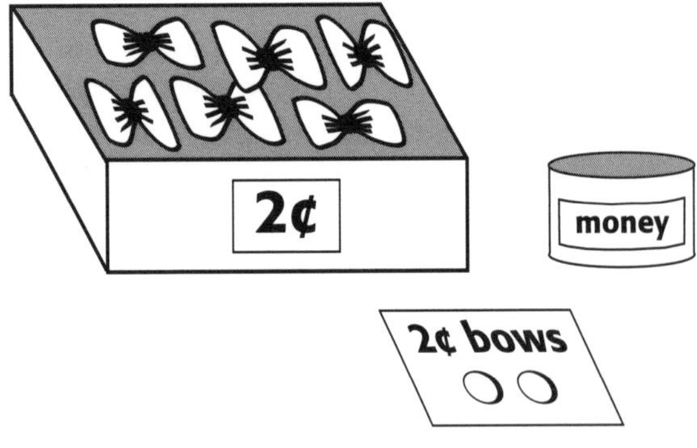

For Younger Children:

Explain that each child will have ten cents to spend. Point to one of the price tags and demonstrate how to read it.

Demonstrate spending your money on valentine decorations with the children's help. Each time you buy an item, place the correct number of pennies on the pay card, put the item in your plastic bag, and then add the pennies to the correct money cup.

When you have spent your money, say that you are ready to make your valentine. Don't model assembling your valentine or the children might want to copy you. Instead, discuss how you might decorate it.

Set up the store in a convenient location. Have the children shop in pairs. Check their purchases to make sure they haven't spent too much or too little. Have them return to the store as needed.

For Older Children:

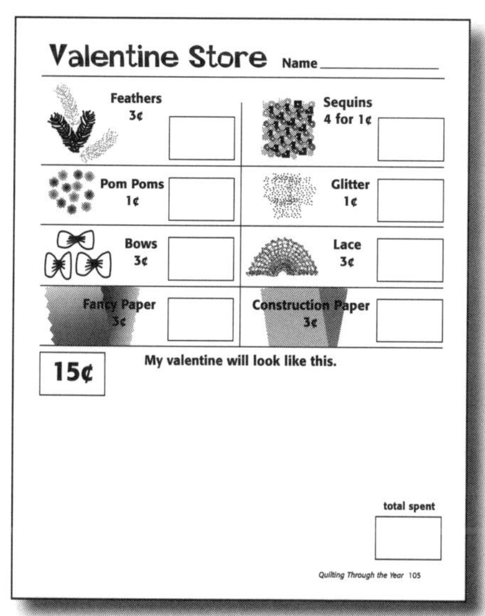

Valentine Store Name

Feathers 3¢	Sequins 4 for 1¢
Pom Poms 1¢	Glitter 1¢
Bows 3¢	Lace 3¢
Fancy Paper 3¢	Construction Paper 3¢

15¢

My valentine will look like this.

total spent

Quilting Through the Year 105

Explain that each child will have fifteen cents to spend. Hand out the store plan blacklines. Explain that the children need to make a plan for what they will buy at the store and how they will design their valentines.

Have fifteen cents (one nickel and one dime) and a container of pennies and nickels for change on hand.

Model how to fill in the store plan.

Teacher: *To show that I plan to buy glitter, I am going to color in the circle and write one cent in the square here.* (She points to the square.) *I'm also going to put one penny in a spent money pile, so I know I've spent a penny. What shall I buy next?*
Children: *Lace. Buy some lace.*
Teacher: *How much is the lace?*
Children: *Three cents.*
Teacher: *Okay, I'm going to circle the lace and write three cents in the square. I'm also going to put three cents in my spent money pile.*

Continue until everyone agrees you have enough items or until you have run out of money. Then explain that each child will have enough money to purchase two of some things. If they choose to do this, they will need to draw a second picture of the item and write the total amount spent in the square.

When you are finished, figure the total, check it by counting the money in your spent money pile, and write the total spent in the square at the bottom of the page.

Point to the area on the blackline where the children can draw a plan for their valentine. Discuss what you might do with the items you purchased, but don't draw your plan or the children might want to copy it.

Give each child fifteen cents and a store plan. Have the children complete their plans at the tables.

Set up the store in a convenient location. Have the children shop in pairs. Most children will follow their plans, but some will not, and that's okay. Check to make sure they haven't spent too much or too little. Have them return to the store as needed.

(end of optional section)

Distribute glue, scissors, and crayons to the tables, and have the children assemble their valentines. When they are done, distribute the 6" red squares and have the children glue the valentines on them. Set the blocks aside to dry.

Assembling the Quilt

Gather the children at the rug. Have the heart quilt blocks and decorated valentine blocks in separate piles. Tell the children you are going to make the quilt in a checkerboard pattern. Explain that the pattern could be heart, valentine, heart, valentine. Ask which block will come first.

Explore counting in multiples while assembling the quilt. See Counting (and Counting in Multiples), page 21, for this discussion.

Heather: *I think a heart will come first.* (She places a heart block on the bulletin board paper.)
Teacher: *What comes next?*
Dakota: *Valentine.* (He places a valentine block next to the heart block.)

Practice pattern skills while laying out each row of the quilt. See Predicting Patterns, page 20, for this discussion.

Call on volunteers to place the blocks on the bulletin board paper in the correct order. Have the class chant the pattern and count the blocks as each one is placed. Make sure to have an odd number of blocks in each row. For example, if you have forty-eight blocks, a good quilt size would be a 5 x 9 rectangle.

See Making Quilt Block Pillows, page 20, for how to turn leftover quilt blocks into a mini art project.

If you have leftover heart or valentine blocks, you can make them into pillows.

Once all the blocks are arranged, glue them on the bulletin board paper, leaving a border.

Searching for Patterns and Designs

Hang the finished quilt on the wall for all to admire. Encourage the children to find designs and patterns hidden in the quilt. You may choose to record their comments on paper idea bubbles and attach them to the quilt.

See Hidden Patterns and Designs, page 22, for a complete discussion of exploring patterns in finished quilts.

Only three of the valentines used lace.
You get the same pattern going down as across.
The valentines all go in diagonal lines.

Heart

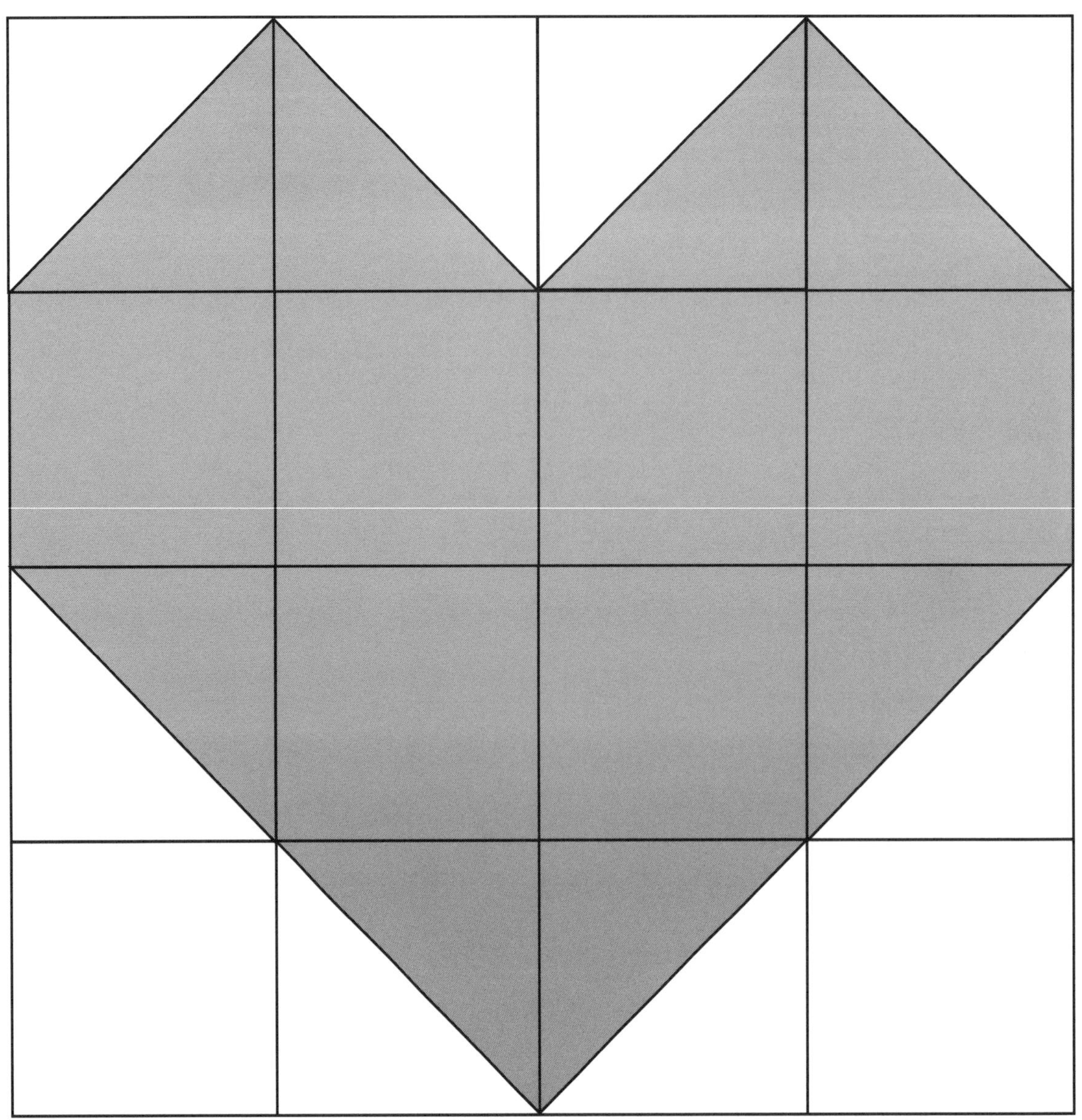

Valentine Store

Name ____________________

Feathers 3¢	**Sequins** 4 for 1¢
Pom Poms 1¢	**Glitter** 1¢
Bows 3¢	**Lace** 3¢
Fancy Paper 3¢	**Construction Paper** 3¢

15¢

My valentine will look like this.

total spent

President's Quilt

16 BLOCK EXAMPLE

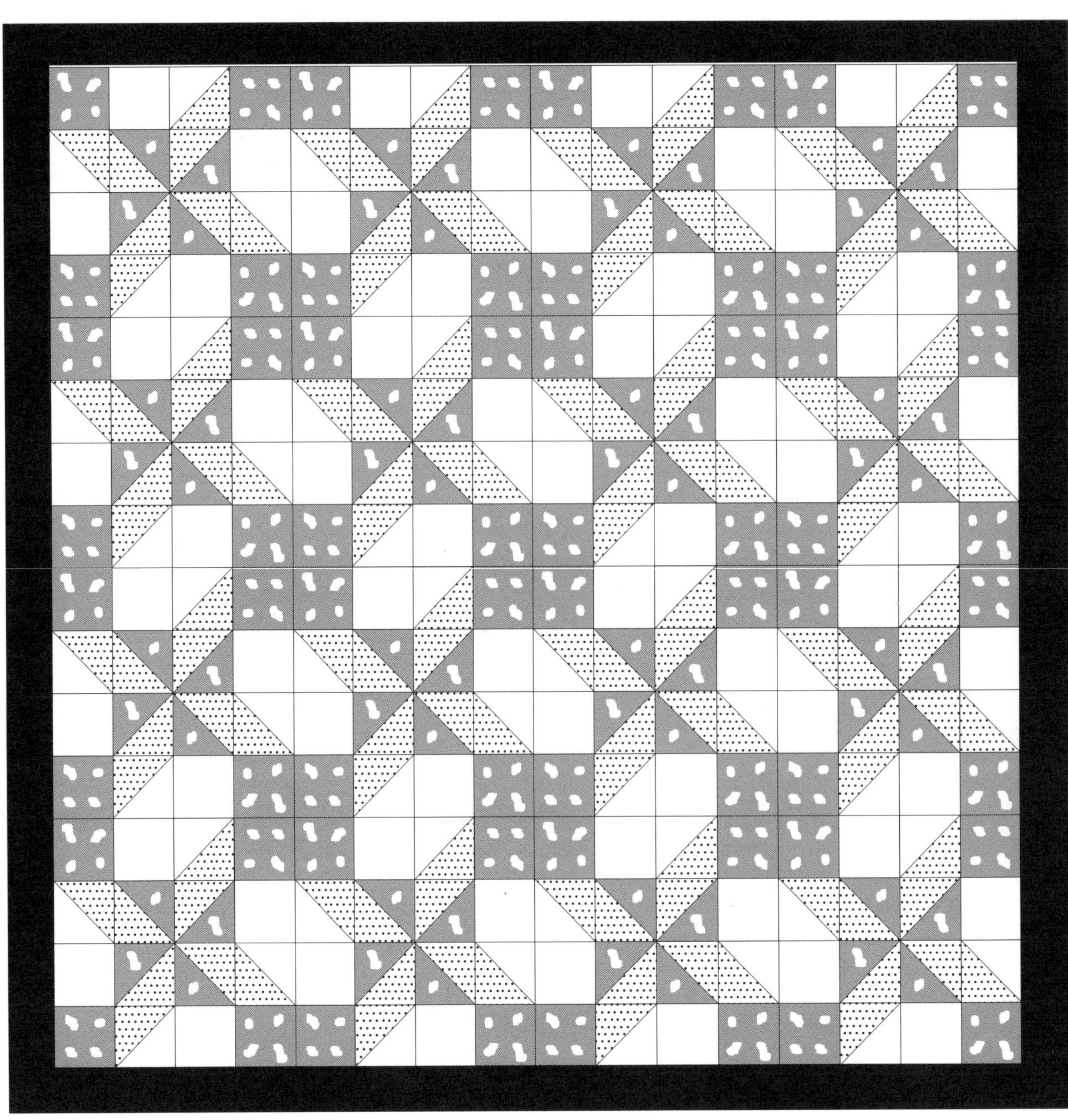

Note: You might need to make extra quilt blocks to complete a row once the quilt design has been selected.

Presidents' Quilt

Lesson Synopsis

Use the optional discussion topics and activities to introduce the presidents' quilt.

Materials Needed

For the introduction (optional)
- books, tapes, and/or videos about Abraham Lincoln and George Washington
- *Presidents Day* by Dianne M. MacMillan
- American flag

The teacher and the class meet at the rug. The teacher introduces the star quilt block that will form the quilt. The children explore the ideas of area and one-half as they learn how to construct the block with the teacher's help. Then they go to the tables to make their own star quilt blocks. When the quilt blocks are dry, the children use white paint and their index fingers to make stars on the blue squares and triangles.

For the teacher and each child to make a star quilt block
- one star blackline, page 111
- six 1½″ squares of royal blue construction paper
- four 1½″ squares of bright red construction paper
- six 1½″ squares of white construction paper
- chalkboard or chart paper (optional for a color key)
- red and blue chalk or markers (optional for a color key)
- scissors and glue
- a sponge soaked with white paint at each work table

Step 2

When the blocks have dried, the children work in small groups to find shapes for the quilt using tiles equal to the number of quilt blocks made by the class. They gather at the rug, share their solutions, and select their favorite as the model for assembling the quilt. The quilt is assembled and glued on the bulletin board paper.

To assemble the quilt
- all the dry star quilt blocks
- 1″ square tiles equal to the number of star quilt blocks
- one large sheet of red bulletin board paper
- glue

Step 3

The quilt is displayed on the wall, and the children discuss patterns they see in it.

Introducing the Quilt

Check out library books, tapes, or videos about George Washington and Abraham Lincoln to share with your students. If possible, start with *Presidents Day* (Best Holiday Books) by Dianne M. MacMillan. Encourage discussion about Washington and Lincoln and explain why Americans celebrate their birthdays each February.

Tell the children they are going to make a presidents' quilt using a star pattern. Point to an American flag and have the children identify the stars and stripes. You might tell the children that the stars in their quilt will have four points, not five.

Making the Star Quilt Block

Overview

▼ Introduce the star blackline.
▼ Children learn how to construct a star quilt block.
▼ Children construct their own star quilt block.

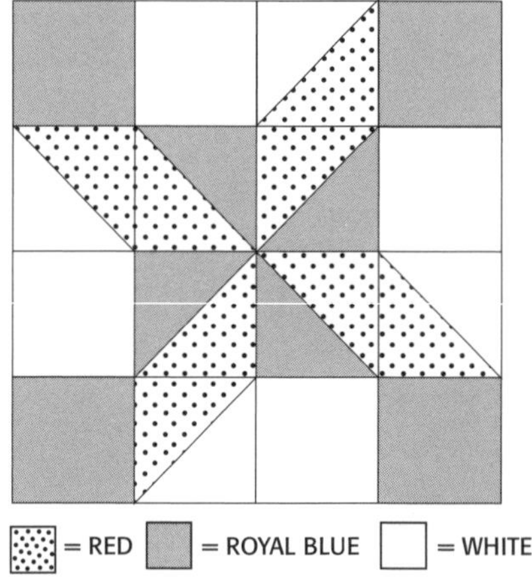

Have the 1½"paper squares, scissors and blacklines on hand.

Note: In this three-color quilt, it is important that the children place the colored paper pieces carefully to maintain the pattern.

Gather the children at the rug. Give each a star blackline. Have the volunteers describe what they see.

Karin: *It looks like a star.*
Thomas: *There is a square in each corner.*
Mary: *Triangles make the points of the star.*
Chris: *Four triangles make a big square in the center of the star.*
Esse: *There will be three colors to go over the shaded, dotted, and white shapes.*

Display some of the red, blue, and white squares and discuss with the children where they should be placed.

Since the star quilt block has a complex design, you may want to make a color key like the one above on the chalkboard or on a piece of chart paper. This way the children will remember that the shaded part is to be blue, the dotted part red, and the white part white.

Teach the ideas that a square is made up of two triangles and that each triangle is half of the square. See Triangles and Halves, page 8, for this discussion.

Point to a shaded triangle in the star. Explain that you have no blue triangles to cover it. Show the children a blue square. Challenge them to find a way to make triangles from the square.

Explore area as you help the children compute the number of squares of each color needed to cover the quilt block. See Early Experiences in Area, page 12, for this discussion.

Ask the children to figure out how many blue squares they will need to cover the shaded parts of the star and background. Have volunteers explain their reasoning.

Teacher: *So, you all agree with Chris that you need six squares to cover the shaded part. I need some volunteers to come and prove it.* (Esse places one blue square in each corner. David asks for scissors and cuts two blue squares to make triangles and places them over the shaded triangles.)
Chris: *See. It took six squares.*

Next, have the children figure out the number of red squares needed and test their predictions.

Finally, have children figure out the number of white squares needed and test their predictions.

Place the colored paper squares and scissors at the tables. Have the children go to their tables to cut and place their squares correctly on to the star blacklines. If you have a color key, remind them to check it.

DON'T put glue on the tables until everyone has placed his or her pieces correctly.

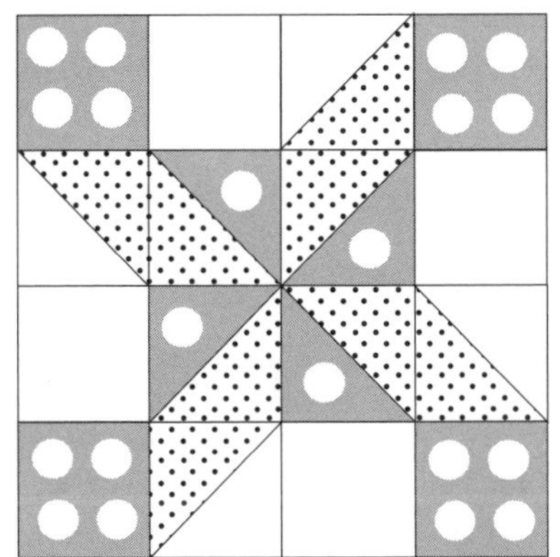

Then distribute glue to the tables. When the children have finished gluing all the squares and triangles in place, have them cut out their quilt blocks carefully around the edges so no white remains. Put the blocks aside to dry.

When the quilt blocks have dried, place sponges soaked with white paint at the tables. Show the children how to make "stars" out of paint on the blue parts of the quilt blocks. Press your index finger into the sponge. Make four dots in each blue square and one dot in each blue triangle.

Distribute the blocks to children, and have them add white paint stars. Once again, put the blocks aside to dry.

Step 2

Assembling the Quilt

Gather the children at the rug. Place the finished star quilt blocks in the center of the rug. Ask the children to estimate how many quilt blocks there are. Then help the children count the blocks. Tell the children that they will use tiles to decide on a good shape for the quilt.

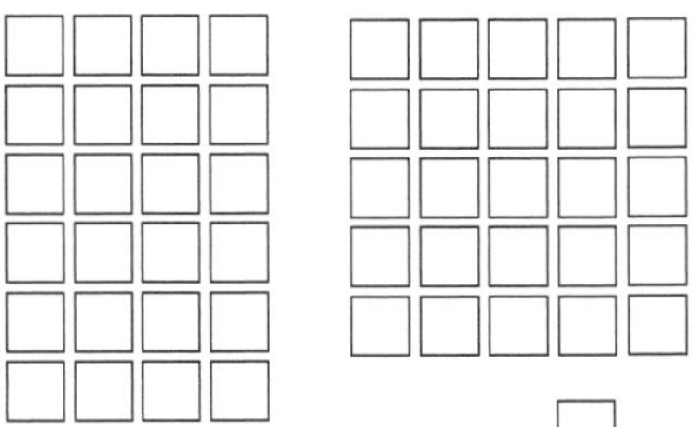

Sometimes the number of quilt blocks does not easily lend itself to a good quilt shape. Brainstorm with the children what might be done to solve this problem. Some possible solutions have been to make more quilt blocks until there are enough to make a good shape, to use left over quilt blocks to make pillows, to leave out the four blocks in the corners so the quilt will "lay right" on the bed, or to make two smaller quilts instead of one large one.

Explore size and shape as you determine the dimensions of the quilt. See Computing the Size of the Quilt, page 17, for this discussion.

Divide them into small groups of two to four. Give each group a set of tiles equal to the number of star quilt blocks made by the class. Have each group experiment to find a good shape for the quilt. As the children think of ideas, let them use the quilt blocks to test their plans.

Explore counting in multiples while assembling the quilt. See Counting (and Counting in Multiples), page 21, for this discussion.

Ask each group to share its favorite shape. Use a tally system of votes to choose the most popular shape.

Lay out the pieces one row at a time. After the first row, have the children predict the number of blocks in each subsequent row.

See Making Quilt Block Pillows, page 20, for how to turn leftover quilt blocks into a mini art project.

If you have leftover blocks, you can make them into pillows.

Glue the blocks on the bulletin board paper, leaving a border.

Searching for Patterns and Designs

See Hidden Patterns and Designs, page 22, for a complete discussion of exploring patterns in finished quilts.

Hang the finished quilt on the wall for all to admire. Encourage the children to find designs and patterns hidden in the quilt. You may choose to record their comments on paper idea bubbles and attach them to the quilt.

Eight triangles make a big square in the center of each star.

Triangles make the points of the stars.

There is a square in each corner of the quilt.

Star

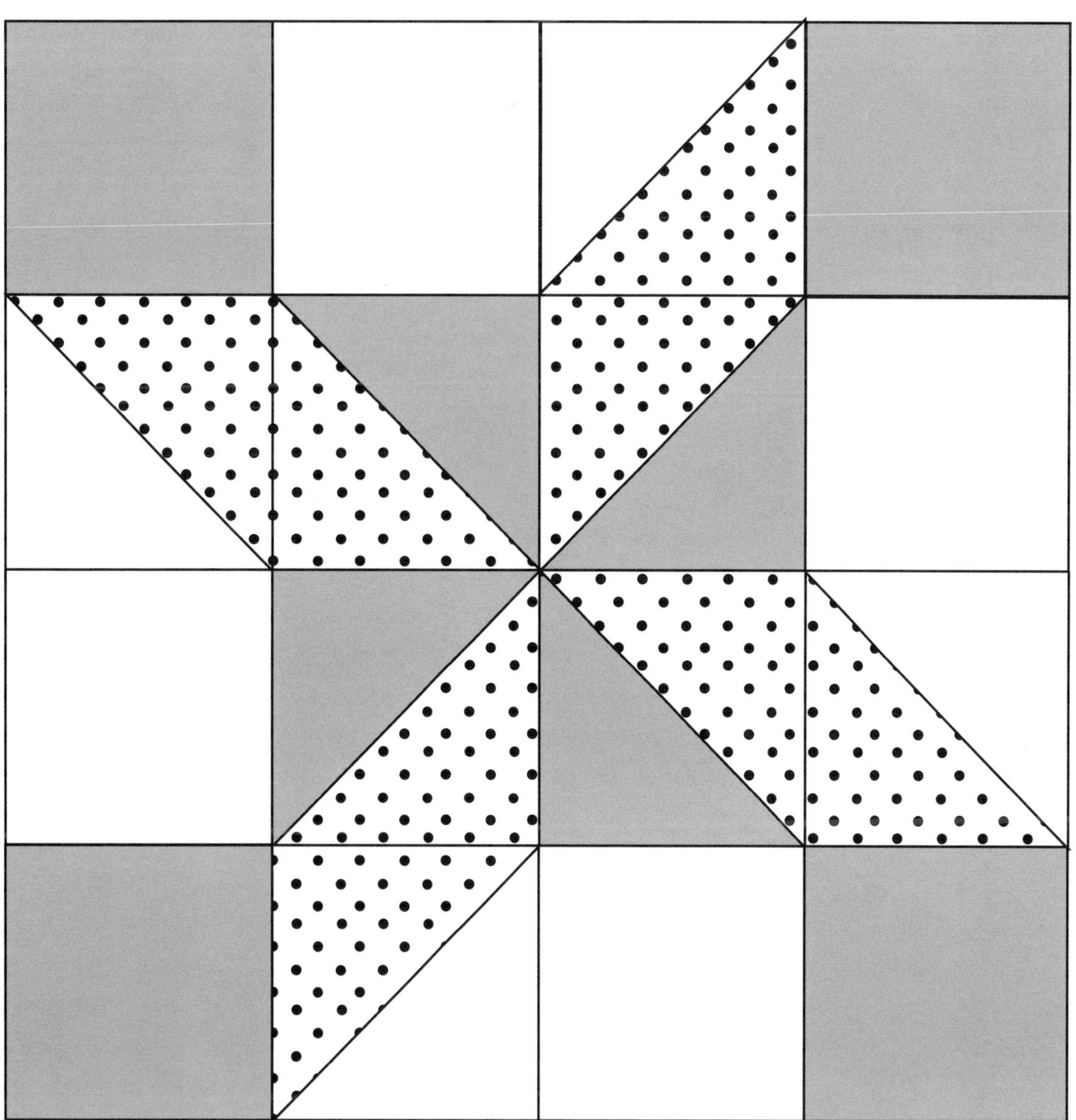

Note: This quilt is assembled from four-block squares. You will need a number of quilt blocks that is divisible by eight (16, 24, 32, etc.). You might need to make extra blocks.

Shamrock Quilt

Lesson Synopsis

Use the optional discussion topics and activities to introduce the shamrock quilt.

The teacher and the class meet at the rug. The teacher introduces the shamrock quilt block that will form the quilt. The children explore the ideas of area, one-half, and one-quarter as they learn how to construct the block with the teacher's help. Then they go to the tables to make their own shamrock quilt blocks.

When the glued blocks have dried, the children work in groups of four to find different patterns in a four-block quilt square. They gather at the rug, share their patterns, and select their favorite. The quilt is assembled from multiples of the selected square and glued on bulletin board paper.

Step 3

The quilt is displayed on the wall, and the children discuss patterns they see in it.

Materials Needed

For the introduction (optional)
- *St. Patrick's Day* by Gail Gibbons
- pictures of shamrocks
- a clover plant
- clover seeds with cups and soil for planting

For the teacher and each child to make a shamrock quilt block
- one shamrock blackline, page 117
- five 2″ squares of green construction paper
- four 2″ squares of yellow construction paper
- one 2¼″ x ½″ strip of green construction paper
- scissors and glue

To assemble the quilt
- all the dry shamrock quilt blocks
- one color cube per child
- one large sheet of green bulletin board paper
- glue

Curriculum Connections

Introducing the Quilt

Read and discuss *St. Patrick's Day* by Gail Gibbons. This book explains the history of Saint Patrick and common Irish symbols, such as the shamrock.

Share pictures of shamrocks or draw one on the board. Invite the children to describe the plant, to look for it outdoors, and to draw pictures of it.

As another option, you can grow white clover, the Irish shamrock, in a sunny window of your classroom. The seeds are available at many nurseries. Your class can plant the seeds in a seed starter tray or in individual cups.

Tell the children they are going to make a shamrock quilt for St. Patrick's Day.

Note: This can be a tricky quilt to make with kindergartners. It is the first quilt of the year that requires the children to figure out how to cut a triangle in half to make two new triangles that are each one-fourth the size of the square.

Making the Shamrock Quilt Block

Overview

- ▼ Introduce the shamrock blackline.
- ▼ Children learn how to construct a shamrock quilt block.
- ▼ Children make their own shamrock quilt blocks.

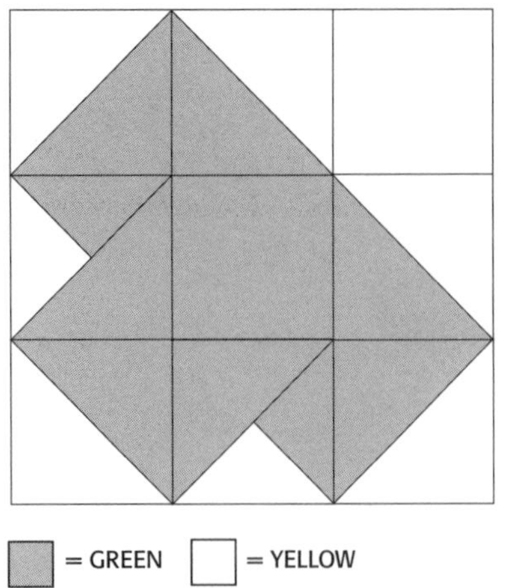

Have the 2″ paper squares, green paper strips, scissors and blacklines on hand.

Gather the children at the rug. Give each a shamrock blackline. Have volunteers describe what they see.

Alan: *It looks like a hat.*
Karin: *There are squares and triangles.*
Thomas: *There are two different colors. White and dotted.*
Mary: *Two of the triangles are small.*

Display yellow and green squares. Ask the children where they think the colors should be placed.

Sean: *I think green goes over the shaded part, because that part is the shamrock.*
Teacher: *What about the yellow squares?*
David: *They will go around the shamrock.*

Explore the ideas that a square is made up of two triangles and that each triangle is half of the square. See Triangles and Halves, page 8, for this discussion.

Explore the ideas that one of the triangles is made up of two smaller triangles and that each small triangle is a quarter of the square. See Triangles and Quarters, page 10, for this discussion.

Point to a large shaded triangle in the shamrock. Explain that you have no triangles to cover it. Show the children a green square. Challenge them to find a way to make triangles from the square.

Ask a volunteer to point to a small shaded triangle in the shamrock. Explain that you also need these small triangles to finish the quilt block. Challenge the children to find a way to make two equal triangles from a large triangle.

Ask the children to figure out how many green squares they will need altogether to cover the shamrock. Have volunteers explain their reasoning.

Teacher: *So, you all agree with Alan that you need five squares to cover the shamrock. I need some volunteers to come and prove it.* (Sara places a green square over the one shaded square on the blackline. Alan asks for scissors and cuts each of the four remaining green squares in half and places seven of the triangles over the large shaded triangles. Micheleen cuts the remaining triangle in half and places it correctly over the small shaded triangle.)
Alan: *See. Five squares. It took five squares.*

Explore area as you help the children compute the number of squares of each color needed to cover the quilt block. See Early Experiences in Area, page 12, for this discussion..

Next, have the children figure out the number of yellow squares needed for the background and test their predictions.

Show the children a strip of green paper and ask where it belongs. (It goes diagonally from the shamrock to the corner of the blackline to make a stem.)

DON'T put glue on the tables until everyone has placed his or her pieces correctly.

Place the paper squares, green paper strips, and scissors at the tables. Have the children go to their tables to cut and place their squares correctly onto the shamrock blacklines.

Then distribute glue to the tables. When the children have finished gluing all the squares and triangles in place, have them glue on the green stems. Then the children should cut out their quilt blocks carefully around the edges so no white remains. Put the blocks aside to dry.

Step 2

Assembling the Quilt

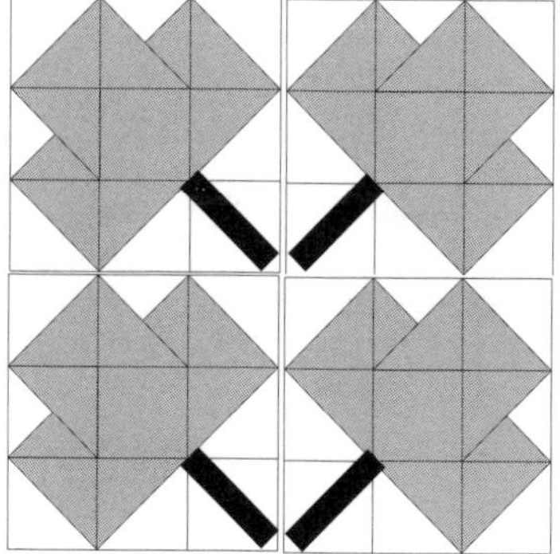

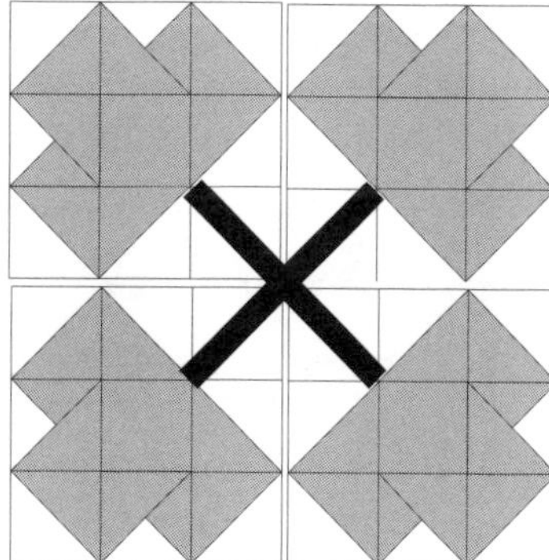

Divide the children into groups of four and give each group four of the finished shamrock quilt blocks. Show how to place the blocks together to make a four-block quilt square. Demonstrate rotating the blocks in different ways to create new designs.

Help children discover patterns in the four-block quilt squares. See Slides and Rotations, page 14, for this discussion.

Encourage groups to experiment rotating the blocks to find a variety of designs. Allow time for the children to walk around and see other groups' designs.

Ask each group to arrange its favorite four-block design in the center of the rug. Give each child a color cube. Explain that each person may cast one vote for his or her favorite design by placing a color cube on that design. Each group then builds the selected quilt square from its four blocks.

See Making Quilt Block Pillows, page 20, for how to turn leftover quilt blocks into a mini art project.

If you have leftover blocks, you can make them into pillows.

Arrange all the quilt squares on the bulletin board paper to make the finished design. Glue the quilt on the bulletin board paper, leaving a border.

Searching for Patterns and Designs

See Hidden Patterns and Designs, page 22, for a complete discussion of exploring patterns in finished quilts.

Hang the finished quilt on the wall for all to admire. Encourage the children to find designs and patterns hidden in the quilt. You may choose to record their comments on paper idea bubbles and attach them to the quilt.

I see upside down V's.

The stems touch each other in the middle.

I see big and little diamonds.

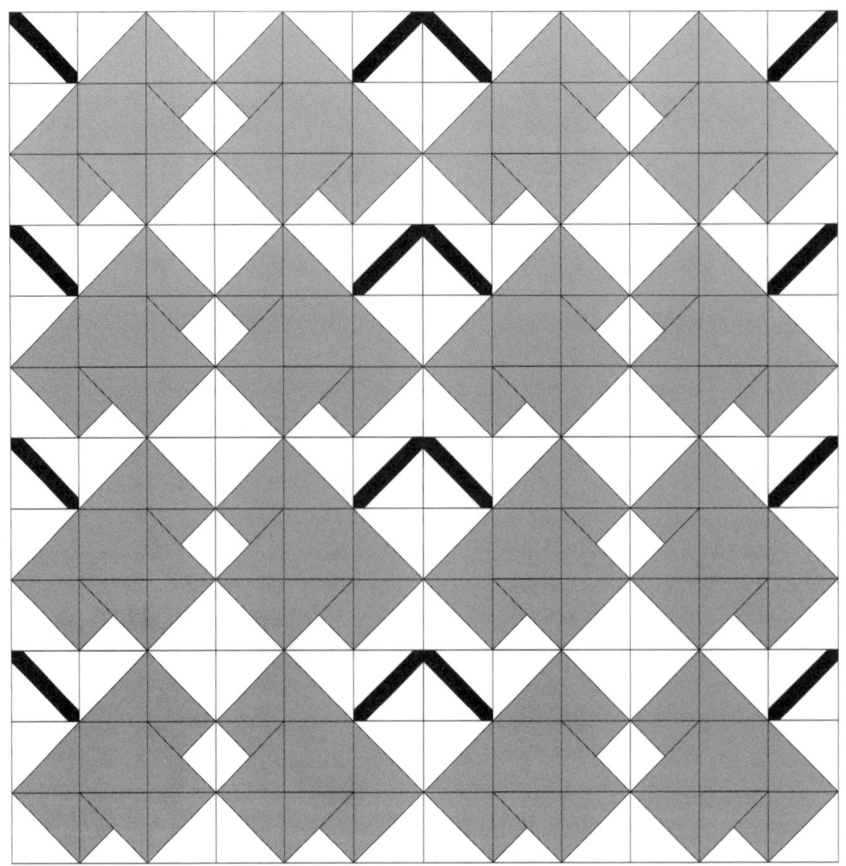

Shamrock

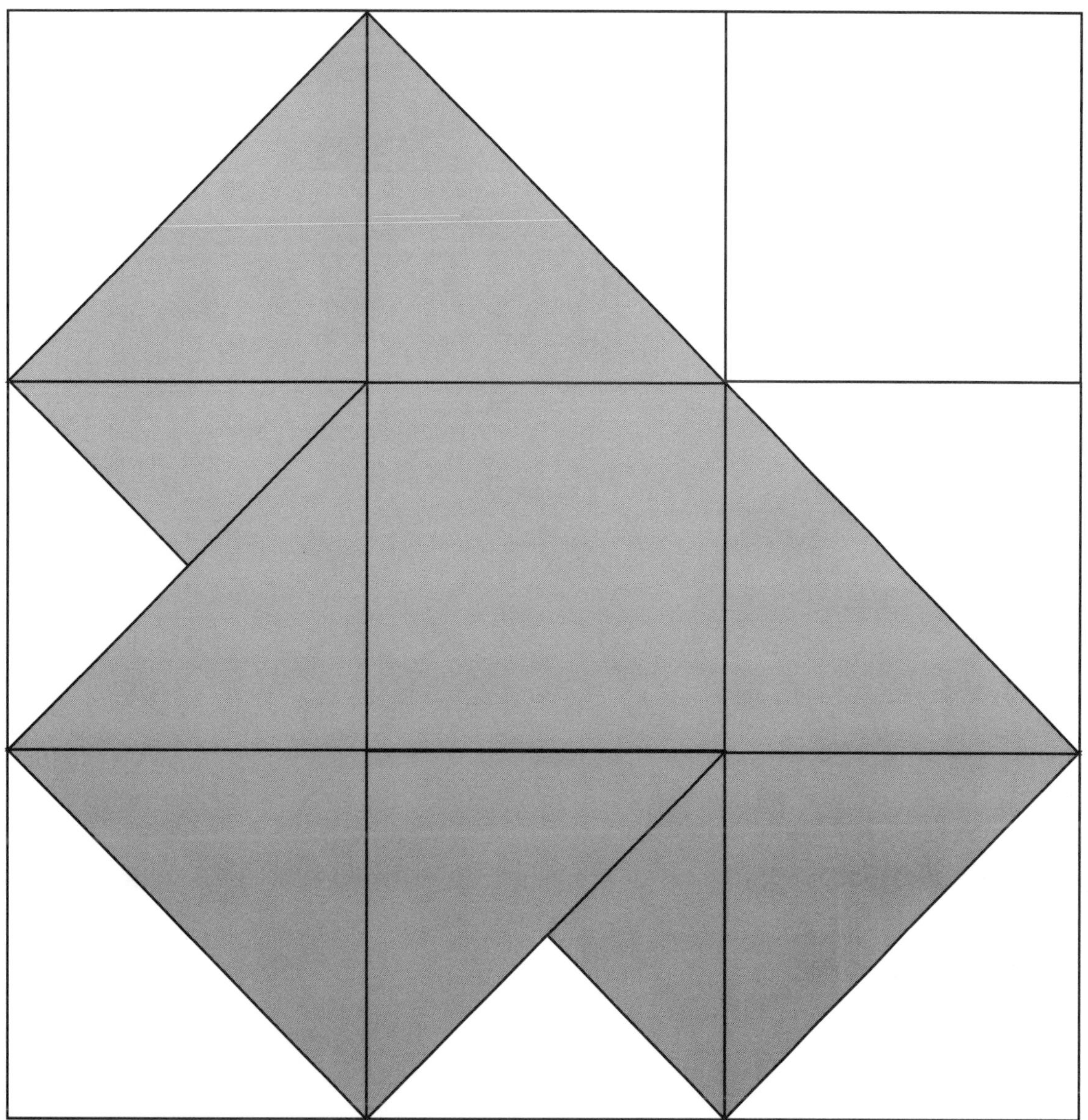

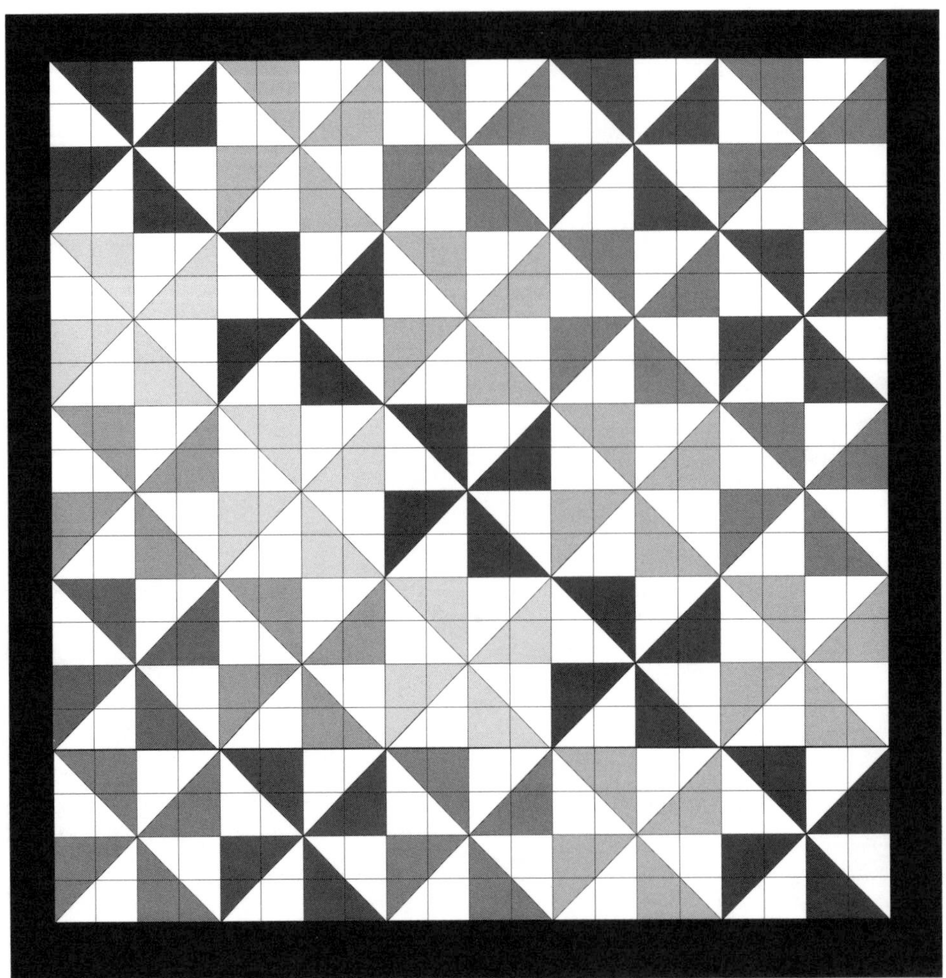

Note: The pinwheels in this quilt should be of several different colors. You will need to decide ahead of time which colors you would like to use, then cut enough squares to match your choices. Each pinwheel requires eight squares of a given color as well as eight white squares.

Pinwheel Quilt

Lesson Synopsis	Materials Needed
Use the optional discussion topics and activities to introduce the pinwheel quilt.	**For the introduction (optional)** • *Did You Hear Wind Sing Your Name? An Oneida Song of Spring* by Sandra De Coteau Orie • other books about March weather, pinwheels, or wind (see bibliography)

The teacher and the class meet at the rug. The teacher introduces the pinwheel quilt block that will form the quilt. The children explore the concepts of area and one-half as they learn how to construct the block with the teacher's help. Then they go to the tables to make their own pinwheel quilt blocks.	**For the teacher and each child to make a pinwheel quilt block:** • one pinwheel blackline, page 123 • eight 1½″ squares of white construction paper • eight 1½″ squares of one bright color (the finished quilt should include a variety of colors) • scissors and glue

When the glued blocks have dried, the children use color counters to find color patterns for the quilt. They gather at the rug, share their patterns, and select their favorite as the model for assembling the quilt. The quilt is assembled and glued on bulletin board paper.	**For the teacher and each child or pair:** • color counters equal to the pinwheel quilt blocks in number and color **To assemble the quilt:** • all the dry pinwheel quilt blocks • cards for labeling (one for each color) • one color cube per child • one large sheet of light blue bulletin board paper • glue

The quilt is displayed on the wall. The children use a paper window frame to find and discuss patterns they see in it.	**For the pattern discussion:** • one 9″ x 9″ sheet of construction paper with a 6″ square cut in the center

Introducing the Quilt

Read and discuss books on springtime. You might take this opportunity to do a mini lesson on wind.

Three books listed in the bibliography help children experience spring in three ways: spiritually through the Native American poem in *Did You Hear Wind Sing Your Name?* by Sandra De Coteau Orie, imaginatively through Pat Hutchins' amusing tale, *The Wind Blew*, and scientifically through *Weather Experiments* by Vera Webster.

Tell the children they are going to make a pinwheel quil, based on a popular quilt pattern. Since this is a springtime quilt, it will be very colorful.

Making the Pinwheel Quilt Block

Overview

- ▼ Introduce the pinwheel blackline.
- ▼ Children learn how to construct a pinwheel quilt block.
- ▼ Children make their own pinwheel quilt blocks.

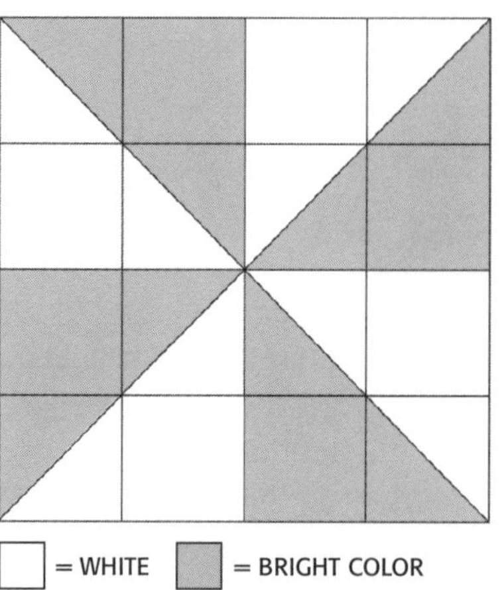

Have the $1\frac{1}{2}$"paper squares, scissors and blacklines on hand.

Gather the children at the rug. Give each a pinwheel blackline. Have volunteers describe what they see.

Andrew: *It is all big triangles.*
Mary: *I think there are only two colors in this quilt, because there are only white and shaded triangles.*
Samantha: *Each big triangle is made of a square and two triangles.*

Explore the ideas that a square is made up of two triangles and that each triangle is half of the square. See Triangles and Halves, page 8, for this discussion.

Display white squares and squares of one bright color. Ask the children where they think the two colors should be placed. (The bright color covers the shaded pinwheel in the blackline; the white covers the white background.)

Explore area as you help children compute the number of squares of each color needed to cover the quilt block. See Early Experiences in Area, page 12, for this discussion.

Point to a shaded triangle in the pinwheel. Explain that you have no triangles to cover it. Show the children a brightly colored square. Challenge them to find a way to make triangles from the square.

Ask the children to figure out how many brightly colored squares they will need altogether to cover the pinwheel. Have volunteers explain their reasoning and test their predictions.

Next, have children figure out the number of white squares needed and test their predictions. Ask them what they notice about the color shapes and white shapes. (Possible answers: They are the same size; they use the same number of squares or triangles.)

DON'T put glue on the tables until everyone has placed his or her pieces correctly.

Assign or have each child choose one bright color for his or her pinwheel. Place the paper squares and scissors at the tables. Have the children go to their tables to cut and place their squares correctly onto the pinwheel blacklines.

Then distribute glue to the tables. When the children have finished gluing all the squares and triangles in place, have them cut out their quilt blocks carefully around the edges so no white remains. Put the blocks aside to dry.

Assembling the Quilt

Gather the children at the rug. Place the finished pinwheel quilt blocks in the center of the rug. Ask the children to sort the blocks by color. Have them help you make a label for each color.

Challenge the children to find interesting color patterns for the quilt blocks. They can work individually or with partners. Tell them to find color counters (unifix cubes, color tiles, etc.) in the room with which to build their patterns. See page 19 for a discussion of building quilt patterns from linear patterns.

Ask each group to arrange its favorite design in the center of the rug. Give each child a color cube. Explain that each person may cast one vote for his or her favorite design by placing a color cube on that design.

Explore pattern and size. See Computing the Size of the Quilt, page 17, for this discussion.

Work with the children to arrange color counters into a rectangle in the selected pattern. Help them notice how the pattern continues in each row.

Explore counting in multiples while assembling the quilt. See Counting (and Counting in Multiples), page 21, for this discussion.

Using the color counters as a model, lay out the pinwheel quilt blocks one row at a time. After the first row, have the children predict the order of the blocks in each subsequent row. Have them chant the pattern as each block is added. Glue the blocks on the bulletin board paper, leaving a border.

Searching for Patterns and Designs

See Hidden Patterns and Designs, page 22, for a complete discussion of exploring patterns in finished quilts.

Lay the finished quilt in the center of the rug. Place the paper window frame on the quilt to isolate different designs. Have the children describe what they see. You may choose to record their comments on paper idea bubbles and attach them to the quilt. Hang the quilt on the wall for all to admire.

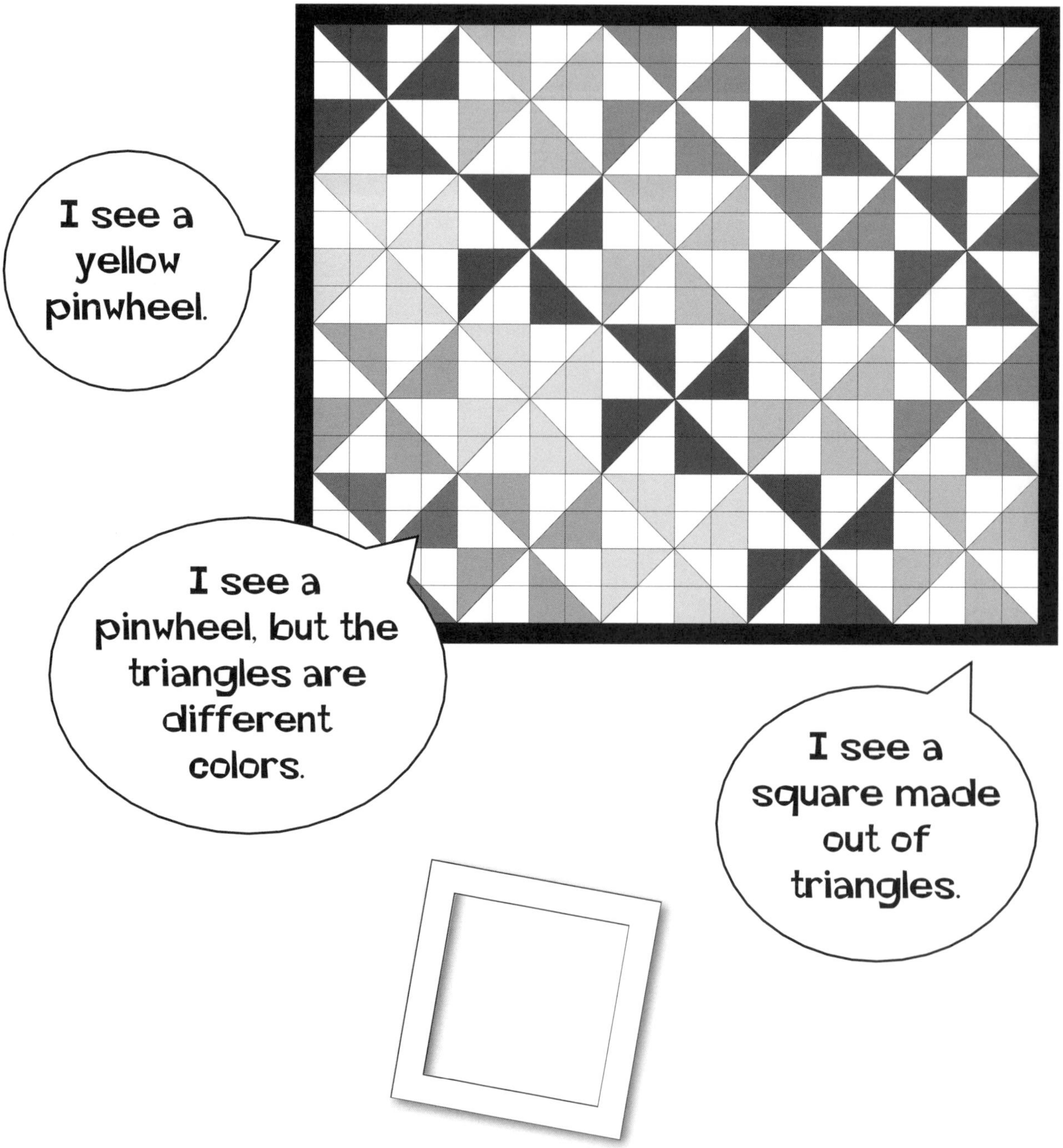

I see a yellow pinwheel.

I see a pinwheel, but the triangles are different colors.

I see a square made out of triangles.

Pinwheel

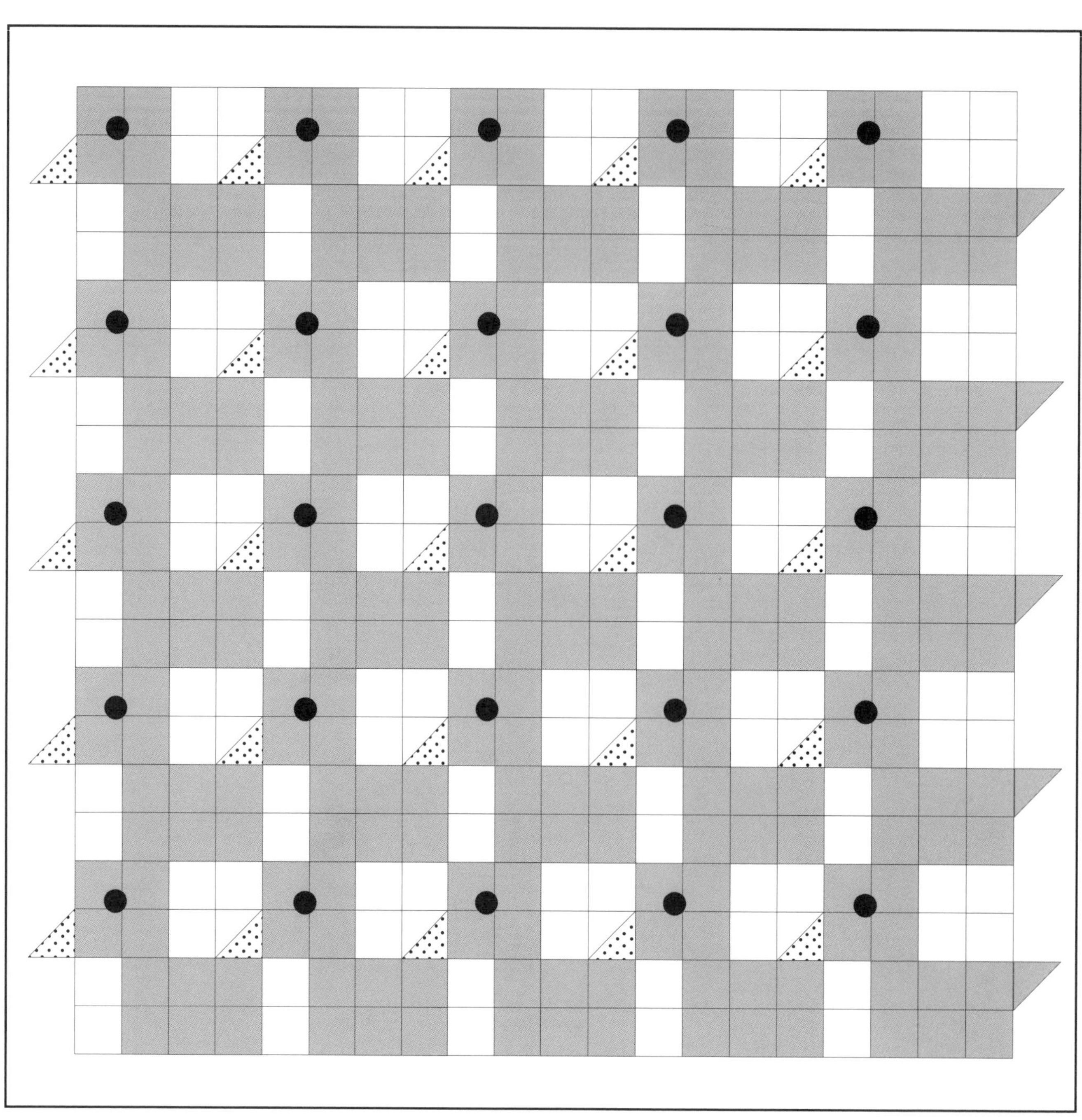

Note: Once you have determined the size of the quilt, you might need to make extra quilt blocks to complete a row.

Chick Quilt

Lesson Synopsis

Use the optional discussion topics and activities to introduce the chick quilt.

The teacher and the class meet at the rug. The teacher introduces the chick quilt block that will form the quilt. The children explore the concepts of area and one-half as they learn how to construct the block with the teacher's help. Then they go to the tables to make their own chick quilt blocks.

When the glued blocks have dried, the children work in small groups to find good shapes and patterns for the quilt using tiles equal to the number of quilt blocks made by the class. They gather at the rug, share their solutions, and select their favorite as the model for assembling the quilt. The children count in multiples as they assemble the quilt and glue it on bulletin board paper.

The quilt is displayed on the wall, and the children discuss patterns they see in it.

Materials Needed

For the introduction (optional)
Good Morning, Chick! by Mirra Ginsburg

For the teacher and each child to make a chick quilt block
- one chick blackline, page 129
- ten 1½″ squares of yellow construction paper
- six 1½″ squares of light blue construction paper
- one 1½″ square of orange construction paper
- one ½″ diameter circle of black construction paper
- scissors and glue

For the teacher and each small group
- 1″ square tiles equal to the number of chick quilt blocks

To assemble the quilt
- all the chick quilt blocks
- one large sheet of light blue bulletin board paper
- five to ten 1½″ squares of light blue, yellow, and orange construction paper to complete the chicks
- glue

Curriculum Connections

Introducing the Quilt

This quilt lesson can provide a great introduction to spring, especially if you incubate chicken or duck eggs in your classroom.

Read and discuss *Good Morning, Chick!* by Mirra Ginsburg. The children can memorize its simple, repetitive language and will enjoy the bright, straightforward illustrations.

Show children pictures of chicks. After discussing what chicks look like and the development process from egg to chick, tell the children they are going to make a chick quilt.

Making the Chick Quilt Block

Overview

- ▼ Introduce the chick blackline.
- ▼ Children learn how to construct a chick quilt block.
- ▼ Children make their own chick quilt blocks.

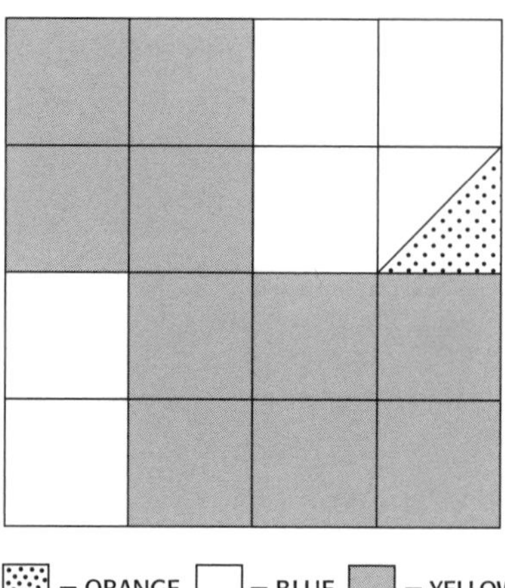

Have the 1½″ paper squares, black paper circle, scissors and blacklines on hand.

Gather the children at the rug. Give each a chick blackline. Have volunteers describe what they see.

Alipate: *I can see a head and a body, but the beak is in the wrong place.*
Nathaniel: *Yeah, the beak can't be on the chick's back.*
Teacher: *I think this quilt will surprise you when it's put together. What else do you notice?*
Miguel: *I see white and gray squares and only one dotted triangle and one white triangle.*
Allison: *I think we will need three colors to make this block.*

Display some of the yellow, light blue, and orange squares. Ask the children where they think the different colors should be placed.

Roxanne: *The yellow squares must go on the dark part to make the head and body.*
Dakota: *The beak is orange, but I don't see where it goes.*
Katherine: *I guess everything else is blue.*

Ask the children how many yellow squares they will need to cover the chick's head and body. Count out the number of squares suggested and test their predictions.

Explore area as you help the children compute the number of squares of each color needed to cover the quilt block. See Early Experiences in Area, page 12, for this discussion.

Explore the ideas that a square is made up of two triangles and that each triangle is half of the square. See Triangles and Halves, page 8, for this discussion.

DON'T put glue on the tables until everyone has placed his or her pieces correctly.

Show the children an orange square. Explain that it will cover the dotted triangle. (You can explain that it will be the beak of the next chick, or you can wait until the quilt is assembled, and let the children be surprised.) Challenge them to find a way to make triangles from the square.

Have the children figure out the number of light blue squares needed to cover the background and test their predictions.

Have volunteers explain their reasoning and test their predictions.

Put the yellow, light blue and orange squares and scissors at the tables. Have the children go to their tables to cut and place the squares correctly onto the chick blacklines.

Then distribute glue to the tables. When the children have finished gluing all the squares and triangles in place, have each child glue on a black circle for the chick's eye. Then the children should cut out their quilt blocks carefully around the edges so no white remains. Put the blocks aside to dry.

Assembling the Quilt

Gather the children at the rug and tell them that they will use tiles to decide on a good size and shape for the quilt. Divide them into small groups of two to four. Give each group a set of tiles equal to the number of chick quilt blocks that have been made by the class.

Have the groups experiment with the tiles to find a good size and shape for the quilt. Ask each group to share its favorite size and shape. Choose one of the shapes for the class's quilt.

Explore counting in multiples while assembling the quilt. See Counting (and Counting in Multiples), page 21, for this discussion.

Once the children have chosen a good size and shape for the quilt, have them lay out the first row on the bulletin board paper in the center of the rug. Ask the children to predict how many blocks there will be once the second row is laid out. Have them share their prediction strategies. As you place the blocks, have the children count aloud to check their predictions. Continue until the entire quilt is laid out.

Once the quilt is assembled, the children will be excited to see that the chicks' beaks are placed correctly. Glue the blocks to the bulletin board paper, leaving a border.

Add orange triangle beaks to the chicks on the left border. Cover the orange beaks on the right border with blue triangles or add yellow triangles for tails (optional).

Searching for Patterns and Designs

See Hidden Patterns and Designs, page 22, for a complete discussion of exploring patterns in finished quilts.

Hang the finished quilt on the wall for all to admire. Encourage the children to find patterns and designs hidden in the quilt. You may choose to record their comments on paper idea bubbles and attach them to the quilt.

It goes yellow square, blue rectangle, yellow square, blue rectangle across.

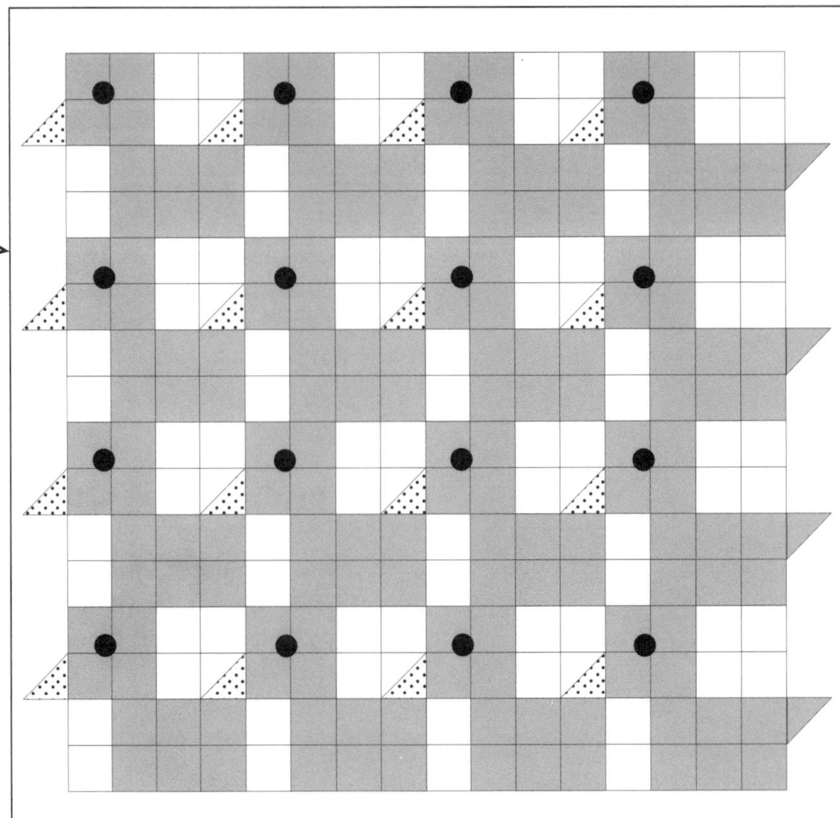

I see squares, rectangles, triangles and circles!

The eyes look like polka dots.

Chick

Flower and Raindrop Quilt

25 BLOCK EXAMPLE

Note: Once the quilt design has been selected, you might need to make extra quilt blocks to complete a row.

Flower and Raindrop Quilt

Lesson Synopsis

Use the optional discussion topics and activities to introduce the flower and raindrop quilt.

The teacher and the class meet at the rug. The teacher introduces the flower quilt block that will form half of the quilt. The children explore the concepts of area, one-half and one-quarter as they learn how to construct the block with the teacher's help. Then they go to the tables to make their own flower quilt blocks.

Step 2

The teacher and the class meet again at the rug. The teacher introduces the raindrop quilt block that will form the other half of the quilt. The children explore the concepts of area, one-half and one-quarter as they learn how to construct the block with the teacher's help. Then they go to the tables to make their own raindrop quilt blocks.

Step 3

When the glued blocks have dried, the children work in small groups to find good shapes and patterns for the quilt using either the finished quilt blocks or reduced copies of the blacklines. They gather at the rug, share their solutions, and select their favorite as the model for assembling the quilt. The quilt is assembled and glued on bulletin board paper.

The quilt is displayed on the wall, and the children discuss patterns they see in it.

Materials Needed

For the introduction (optional)

- *Rain Makes Applesauce* by Julian Scheer
- other books about rain and flowers

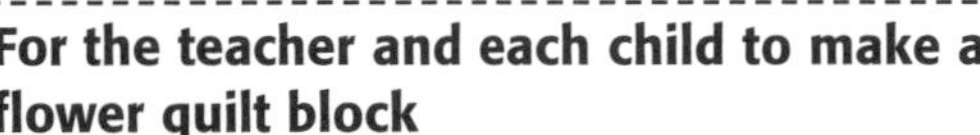

For the teacher and each child to make a flower quilt block

- one April flower blackline, page 136
- eighteen 1″ squares of pink construction paper
- eight 1″ squares of green construction paper
- two 1″ squares of yellow construction paper
- eight 1″ squares of light blue construction paper
- scissors and glue

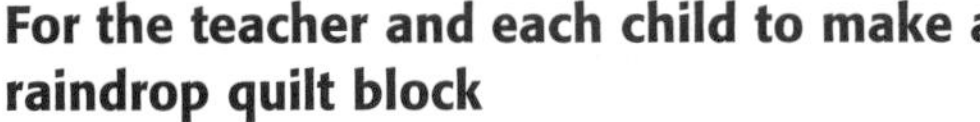

For the teacher and each child to make a raindrop quilt block

- one raindrop blackline, page 137
- sixteen 1″ squares of dark blue construction paper
- twenty-one 1″ squares of light blue construction paper
- scissors and glue

For the teacher and/or each small group

- all the finished flower quilt blocks (or reduced copies of flower blackline, page 130)
- all the finished raindrop quilt blocks (or reduced copies of raindrop blackline, page 130)
- overhead projector (optional)
- scissors

To assemble the quilt

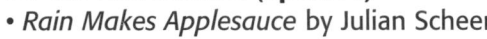

- all the dry flower and raindrop quilt blocks
- one color cube per child
- one large sheet of light blue bulletin board paper
- glue

Curriculum Connections

Introducing the Quilt

Read and discuss books about rain and flowers. If you choose to read *Rain Makes Applesauce* by Julian Scheer, enjoy the book's charming illustrations and silly, delightful text. The repeating line "Oh you're just talking silly talk" draws the children into the reading so much that they request the book again and again.

Discuss why rain is essential to new plant growth, especially during spring. Tell the children they are going to make a quilt of flowers and raindrops.

There are two ways to proceed with this quilt:

Option 1 - Each child can complete both quilt blocks, making a quilt of forty to sixty squares.
Option 2 - Half the students can complete the flower blocks while the other half completes the raindrop blocks.

Once you have decided how large a quilt your class will make, proceed with steps 1 and 2 and distribute the blacklines accordingly.

Making the Flower Quilt Block

Overview

- ▼ Introduce the flower blackline.
- ▼ Children learn how to construct a flower quilt block.
- ▼ Children make their own flower quilt blocks.

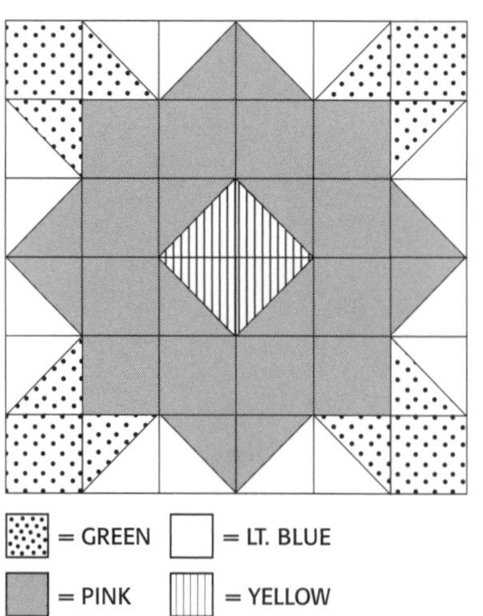

Have the 1″ paper squares, scissors and blacklines on hand.

Gather the children at the rug. Give each a flower blackline. Have volunteers describe what they see.

Rachel: *I see triangles and squares.*
Melissa: *There are four different colors of squares on the flower.*
Tony: *The squares are small.*

Show the children your flower quilt block and a pink square. Ask them where the pink squares go.

Jesse: *I think they cover the shaded squares to make the flower part.*
Teacher: *What about this yellow square?*
Karin: *It goes in the middle to make the middle of the flower.*
Thomas: *The green squares are the leaves; they go over the dotted part in the corners.*
Micheleen: *The blue squares must cover the white part.*

Explore the ideas that a square is made up of two triangles and that each triangle is half of the square. See Triangles and Halves, page 8, for this discussion.

Show the children that you have only squares, no triangles, with which to cover the flower blackline. Challenge them to find a way to make triangles from the squares.

Explore area as you help children compute the number of squares of each color needed to cover the quilt block. See Early Experiences in Area, page 12, for this discussion.

Challenge the children to figure out how many squares of each color they will need to cover the flower.

Count out the number of squares suggested and test their predictions.

Place the paper squares and scissors at the tables. Have the children go to their tables to cut and place their squares correctly onto the April flower blacklines.

DON'T put glue on the tables until everyone has placed his or her pieces correctly.

Then distribute glue to the tables. When the children have finished gluing all the squares and triangles in place, they should cut out their quilt blocks carefully around the edges so no white remains. Put the blocks aside to dry.

Making the Raindrop Quilt Block

Overview

- ▼ Introduce the raindrop blackline.
- ▼ Children learn how to construct a raindrop quilt block.
- ▼ Children make their own raindrop quilt blocks.

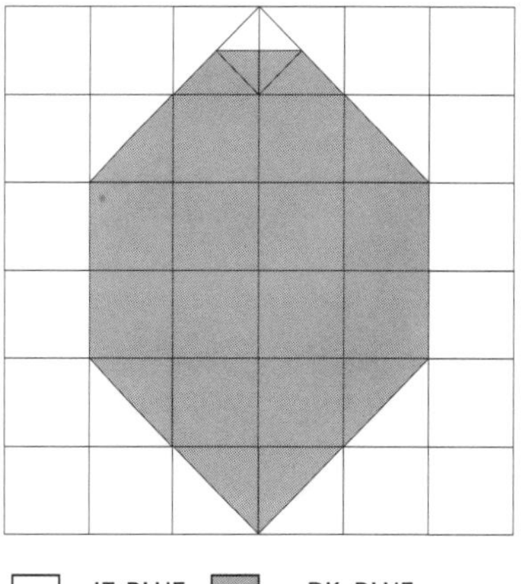

Note: Children will encounter a special challenge in completing the raindrop quilt block. The top of the raindrop is formed with triangles equal to one-quarter the size of the square.

Have the 1″ paper squares, scissors and blacklines on hand.

Gather the children at the rug. Give each a raindrop blackline. Have volunteers describe what they see.

Ask the children to figure out how many squares of each color they will need to cover the raindrop.

Explore the ideas that one of the triangles is made up of two smaller triangles and that each small triangle is a quarter of the square. See Triangles and Quarters, page 10, for this discussion.

Talk about the triangles at the top of the raindrop blackline. Challenge the children to find a way to cut the squares into small triangles to cover this part. Make sure to have extra squares on hand for mistakes. Allow time for children to suggest their ideas and try out methods as a class before you send them to work on their own. If you model this part carefully, the children will do just fine. Whether or not they come up with the easiest solution (cutting the squares into halves and then quarters), they can usually devise rather inventive solutions.

Place the paper squares and scissors at the tables. Have the children go to their tables to cut and place the squares onto the raindrop blacklines.

DON'T put glue on the tables until everyone has placed his or her pieces correctly.

Then distribute glue to the tables. When the children have finished gluing all the squares and triangles in place, have them cut out their quilt blocks carefully around the edges so no white remains. Put the blocks aside to dry.

Assembling the Quilt

This quilt can be assembled with stunning designs. The class should select a design for the quilt using the flower and raindrop images rather than tiles or counters, so experiment with the finished quilt blocks as a class or distribute reduced copies of the two blacklines (see page 130) to small groups of two to four. If you want to model designs, you can make transparencies of the reduced blacklines for the overhead projector.

Use quilt blocks to demonstrate the easiest pattern: raindrop, flower, raindrop, flower. Have the children describe what they see. Then send small groups to the tables to cut out their reduced blacklines, count out the needed blocks, and experiment to find a good design, size and shape and for the quilt. As the children come up with ideas, let them use the finished quilt blocks to test their plans.

Remind the children that quilts are square or rectangular, and that they may not need to use all the quilt blocks to get a good size for the quilt.

Ask each group to arrange its favorite shape and design in the center of the rug. Give each child a color cube. Tell them that each person may cast one vote for his or her favorite design by placing a color cube on that design.

Practice pattern skills while laying out each row of the quilt. See Predicting Patterns, page 20, for this discussion.

While assembling the quilt, have the children predict which quilt block will come next to continue the pattern.

After all the quilt blocks have been placed correctly in the selected pattern, glue them on the bulletin board paper, leaving a border.

See Making Quilt Block Pillows, page 20, for how to turn leftover quilt blocks into a mini art project.

If you have leftover blocks, you can make them into pillows.

Searching for Patterns and Designs

See Hidden Patterns and Designs, page 22, for a complete discussion of exploring patterns in finished quilts.

Hang the finished quilt on the wall for all to admire. Encourage the children to find designs and patterns hidden in the quilt. You may choose to record their comments on paper idea bubbles and attach them to the quilt.

The flowers make a diagonal from corner to corner.

The flowers make a square in the middle of the quilt.

April Flower

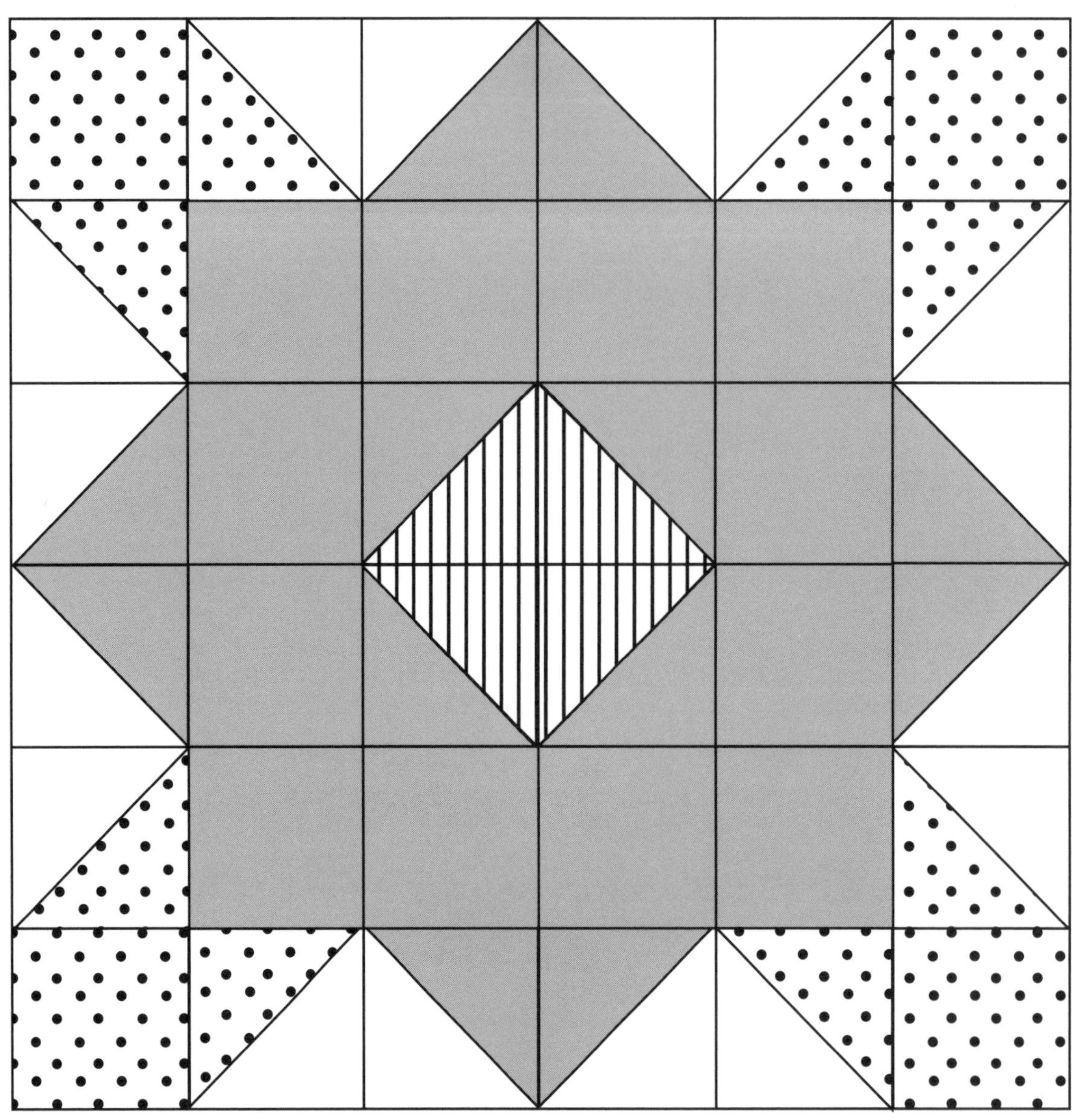

Raindrop

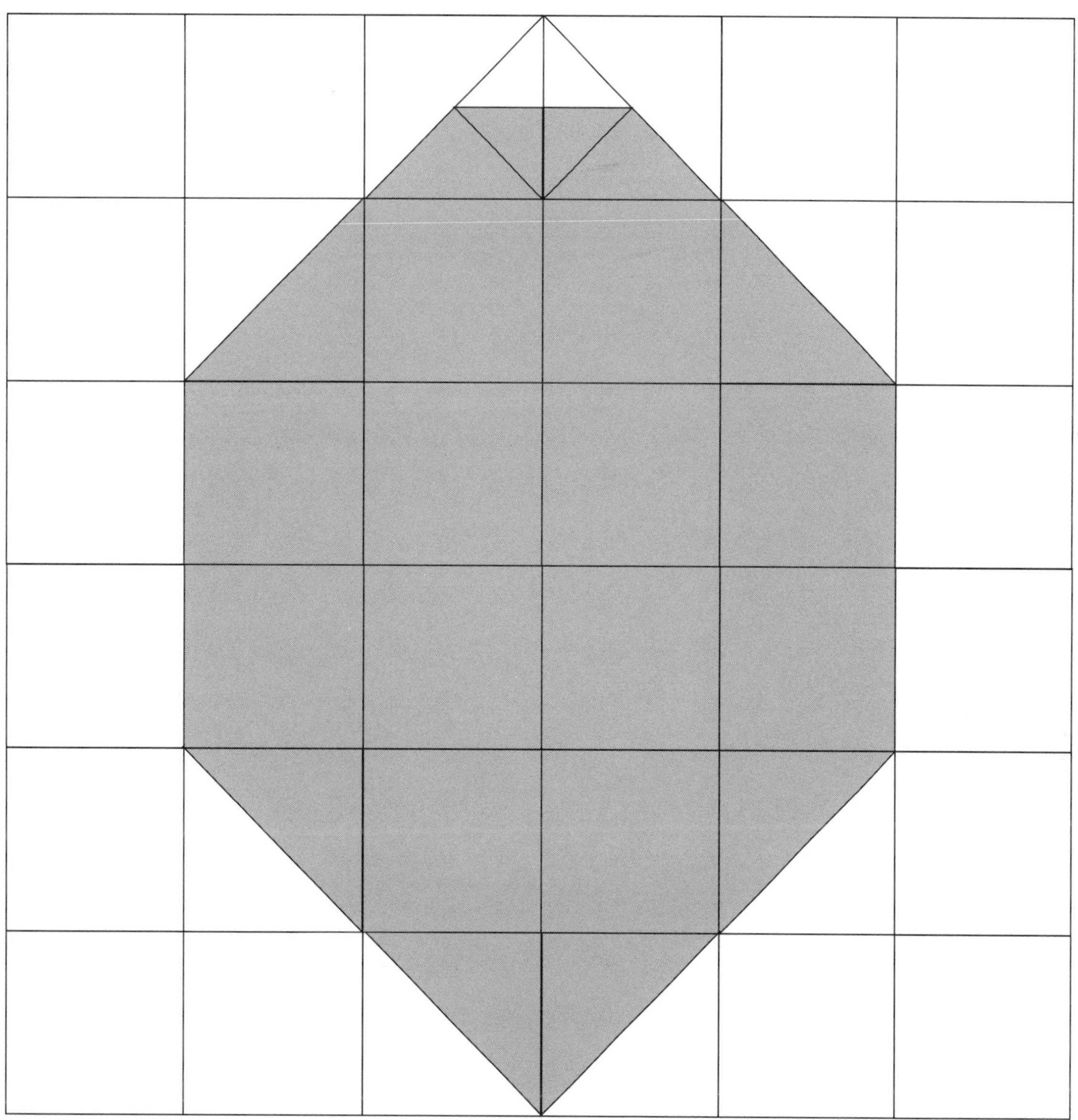

24 BLOCK EXAMPLE

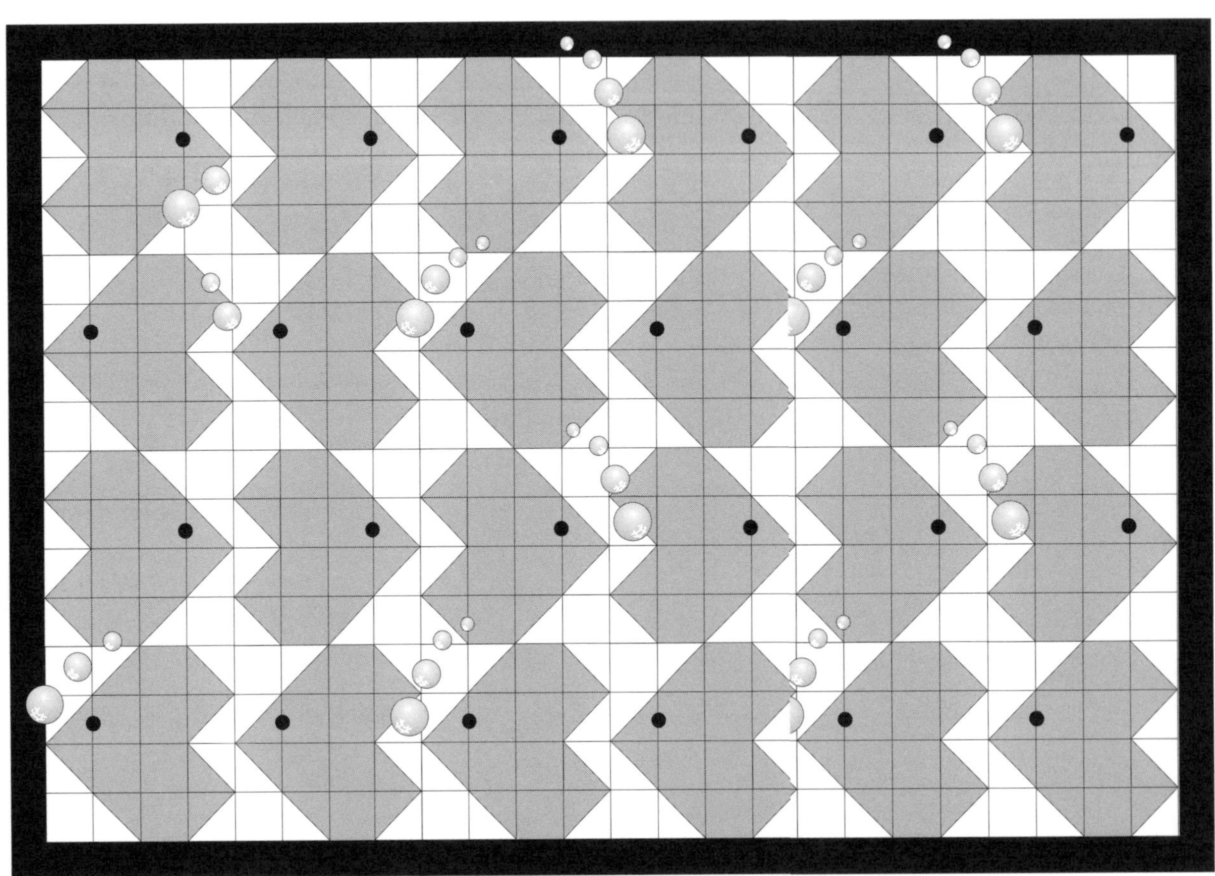

Note: Once you have determined the size of the quilt, you might need to make extra quilt blocks to complete a row.

Rainbow Fish Quilt

Lesson Synopsis

Use the optional discussion topics and activities to introduce the rainbow fish quilt.

Materials Needed

For the introduction (optional)
- *The Rainbow Fish* by Marcus Pfister

Step 1

The teacher and the class meet at the rug. The teacher introduces the rainbow fish quilt block that will form the quilt. The children explore the concepts of area and one-half as they learn how to construct the block with the teacher's help. They create blue water on white paper by painting it with diluted blue watercolor (optional). Then they go to the tables to make their own rainbow fish quilt blocks.

For the class to make watercolored paper (optional)
- two sheets of 12″ x 18″ white construction paper
- one large sheet of white bulletin board paper
- diluted blue watercolor paint
- two child-sized paintbrushes
- two 3″ paintbrushes
- scissors

For the teacher and each child to make a rainbow fish quilt block:
- one rainbow fish blackline, page 143
- six 1½″ squares of blue or blue watercolored construction paper (made with materials listed above)
- ten 1½″ squares of multicolored metallic wrapping paper
- scissors and glue

Step 2

The children work with partners to find shapes and sizes for the quilt using tiles equal to the number of quilt blocks made by the class. They gather at the rug, share their shapes and select their favorite as a model for assembling the quilt. The quilt is assembled and glued on bulletin board paper.

For the teacher and each pair of children:
- 1″ square tiles equal to the number of quilt blocks made by the class

To assemble the quilt:
- all the dry rainbow fish quilt blocks
- blue or blue watercolored bulletin board paper (made with materials listed above)
- one ¾″ black or white button for each rainbow fish
- fish bubbles in various sizes (use lamination remnants or acetate from transparencies)
- clear tape
- glue

Step 3

The quilt is displayed on the wall, and the children discuss patterns they see in it.

Introducing the Quilt

Meet with the children at the rug. Read and discuss *The Rainbow Fish* by Marcus Pfister. Ask how the children feel about the way the rainbow fish is treated. What do they think about his solution to the problem?

Point out the illustrations. Ask if children can guess how the artist made them. If necessary, explain that they were made with watercolors and metallic paper. Tell the children they are going to make a rainbow fish quilt.

Making the Rainbow Fish Quilt Block

Overview:

- ▼ Children paint paper with blue watercolor (optional).
- ▼ Introduce the rainbow fish blackline.
- ▼ Children learn how to construct a rainbow fish quilt block.
- ▼ Children make their own rainbow fish quilt blocks.

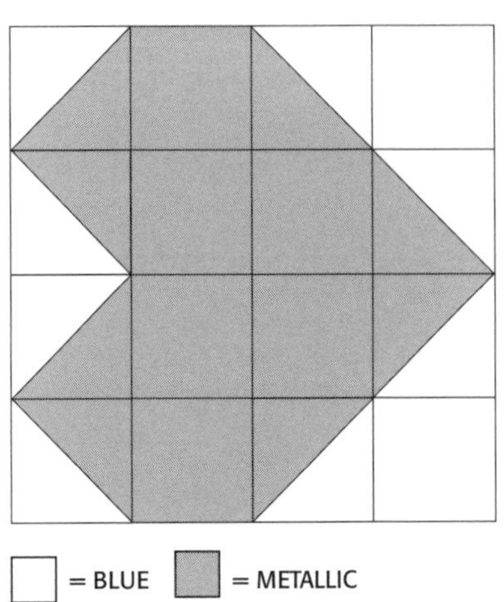

= BLUE = METALLIC

Making the Watercolored Paper (optional)

Note: This is an optional step. You may choose to use blue paper instead.

Have the two sheets of white construction paper and the white bulletin board paper on hand. Show the children how to dip the small brushes in a container of diluted blue watercolor paint and brush it across the construction paper in wide, even strokes. While two volunteers paint the construction paper, allow others to take turns painting the large sheet of bulletin board paper in the same way using the larger brushes. Place the paper aside to dry. When the two sheets of construction paper have dried, cut them into 1½″ squares for the quilt blocks.

Have the 1½″ paper squares, scissors and blacklines on hand.

Gather the children at the rug. Give each a rainbow fish blackline. Have volunteers describe what they see.

Michael: *It looks like a sideways heart.*
Allison: *There are squares and triangles.*
Vanessa: *It looks like an angel fish, too.*
George: *It looks like a fish with his mouth wide open.*
Heather: *There must be two colors to make this quilt.*

Show the children your quilt block and the blue and multicolored metallic squares. Ask the children where they think the different colors should go.

Tiffany: *The blue squares look like water. I think they will make the water around the fish.*
Harold: *The sparkly squares will make the fish, 'cause the rainbow fish is beautiful.*

Explore the ideas that a square is made up of two triangles and that each triangle is half of the square. See Triangles and Halves, page 8, for this discussion.

Explain that you have only squares, no triangles, with which to cover the rainbow fish. Challenge the children to find a way to make triangles from the squares.

Explore area as you help children compute the number of squares of each color needed to cover the quilt block. See Early Experiences in Area, page 12, for this discussion.

Next, ask the children to figure out how many squares of each color they will need to cover the fish. Count out the number of squares suggested and test their predictions.

Place the paper squares and scissors at the tables. Have the children go to their tables to cut and place the squares correctly onto the rainbow fish blacklines.

DON'T put glue on the tables until you are sure children have placed their pieces correctly.

Then distribute glue to the tables. When the children have finished gluing all the squares and triangles in place, have them cut out their quilt blocks carefully around the edges so no white remains. Put the blocks aside to dry.

Assembling the Quilt

Gather the children at the rug. Tell them they are going to use tiles to decide on a good shape for the quilt.

Explore shape and size. See Computing the Size of the Quilt, page 17, for this discussion.

Divide the children into pairs. Give each pair tiles and have them experiment to find a good shape and size for the quilt. Provide help and encouragement as needed. Ask each group to assemble its favorite shape on the rug. Have the children select one of the shapes for the class's quilt.

Once they have decided on a good shape, have them lay out the first row of the quilt on the bulletin board paper, with all the fishes facing in one direction. Every other row of the quilt should go in the opposite direction.

Explore counting in multiples while assembling the quilt. See Counting (and Counting in Multiples), page 21, for this discussion.

Once the second row is laid out, ask the children to predict how many blocks the quilt will have altogether. Encourage children to share their prediction strategies. As the rest of the blocks are placed, have the children count aloud to test their predictions. Continue until the entire quilt is assembled.

Searching for Patterns and Designs

See Hidden Patterns and Designs, page 22, for a complete discussion of exploring patterns in finished quilts.

Hang the quilt on the wall for all to admire. Encourage the children to find designs and patterns hidden in the quilt. You may choose to record their comments on paper idea bubbles and attach them to the quilt.

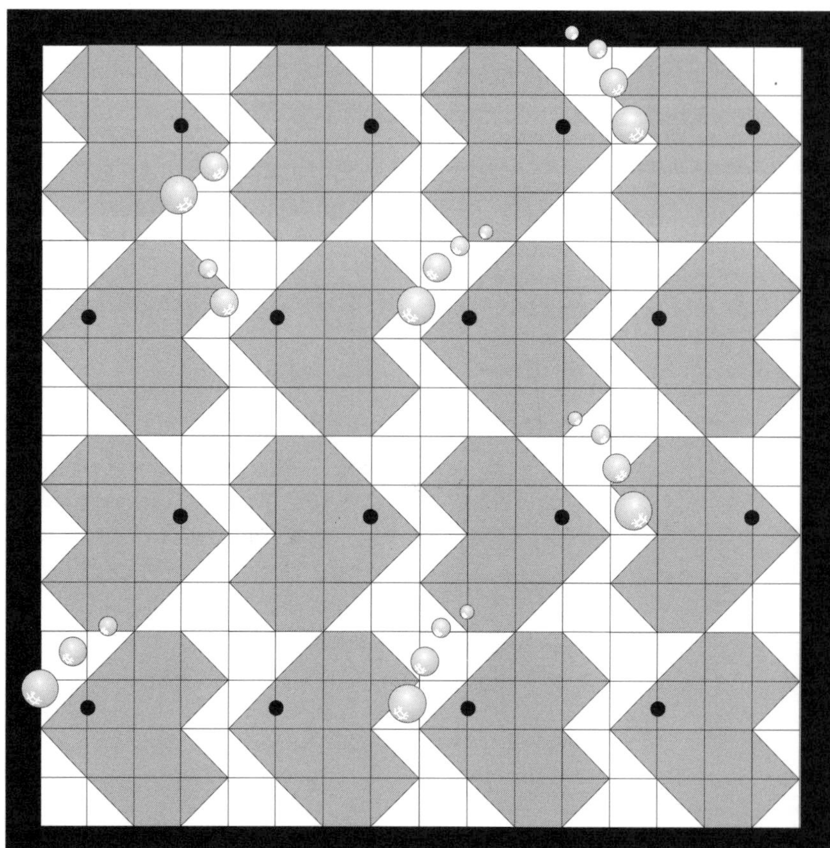

The pattern goes right, left, right, left

There is a blue zig-zag all the way down each row.

The eyes zig-zag too.

Rainbow Fish

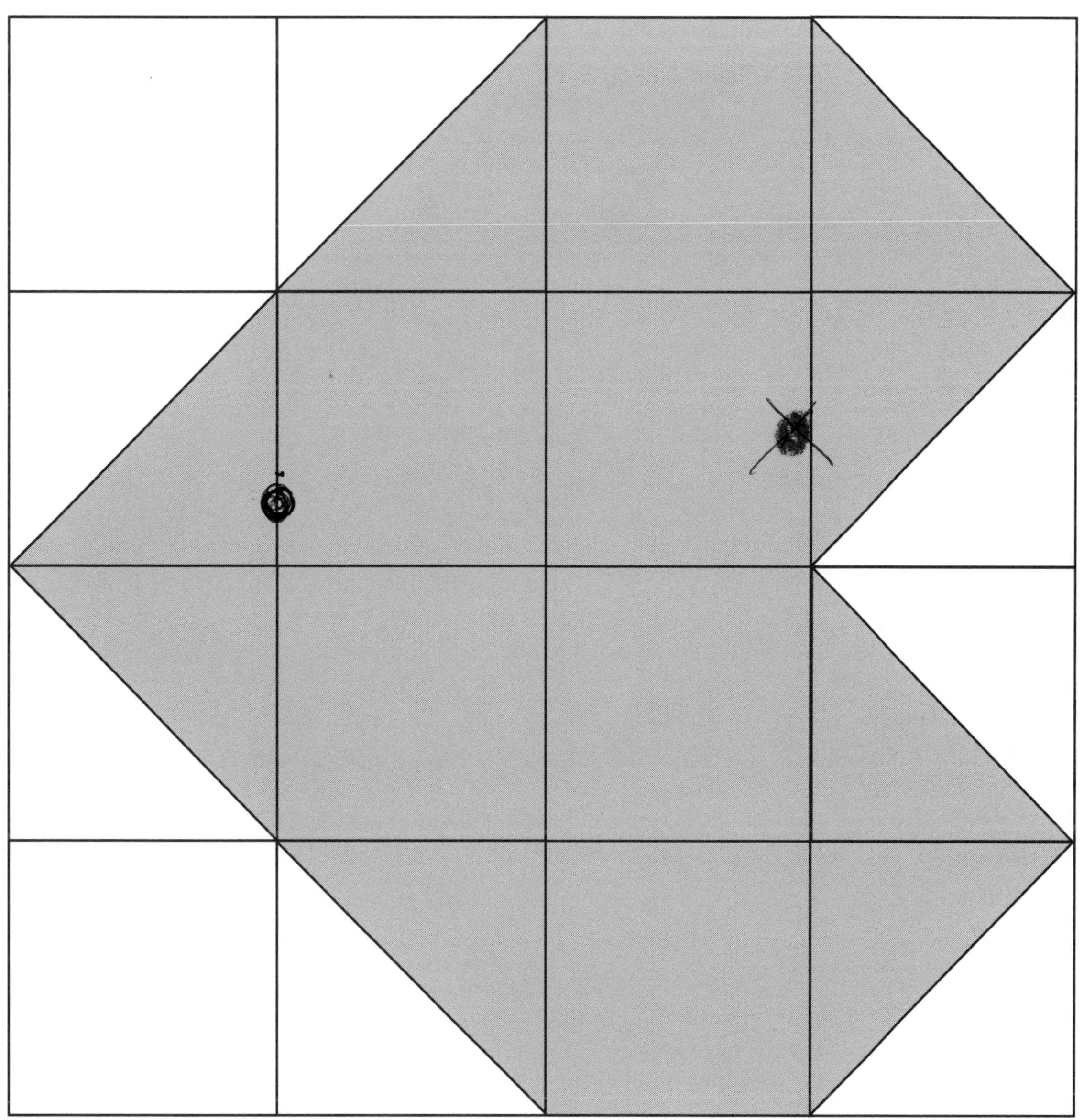

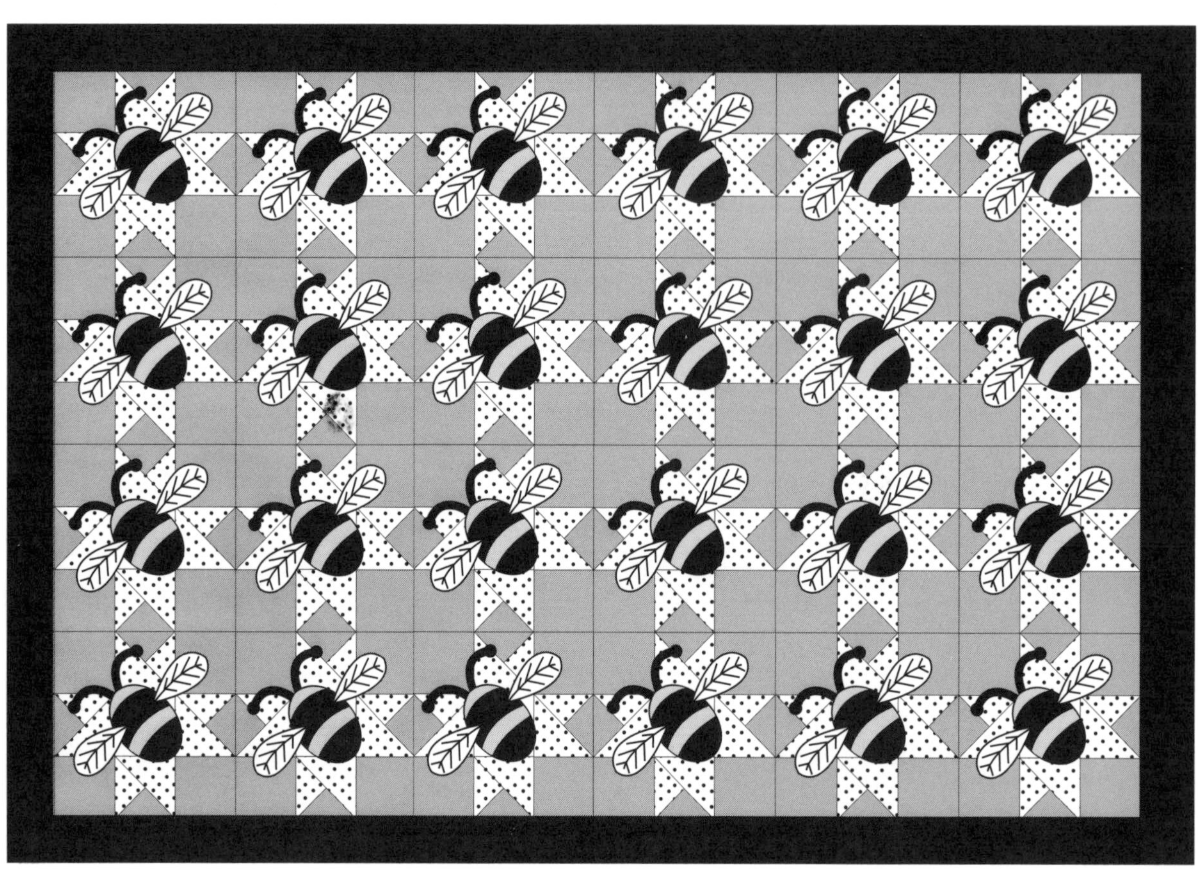

Note: Once you have determined the size of the quilt, you might need to make extra quilt blocks to complete a row.

Flower and Bee Quilt

Lesson Synopsis

Use the optional discussion topics and activities to introduce the flower and bee quilt.

The teacher and the class meet at the rug. The teacher introduces the flower quilt block that will form half of the quilt. The children explore the concepts of area, one-half and one-quarter as they learn how to construct the block with the teacher's help. Then they go to the tables to construct their own flower quilt blocks.

Note: You may point out that this is a different flower quilt block than the one they made for the raindrop and flower quilt in April.

The teacher and the class meet again at the rug. The children learn how to construct tissue paper bees. They make their own bees and glue them on the flower quilt blocks.

When the glued blocks have dried, the children work with the teacher to find good shapes and sizes for the quilt. The quilt is assembled and glued on bulletin board paper.

The quilt is displayed on the wall, and the children discuss patterns they see in it.

Materials Needed

For the introduction (optional)
- *The Rose in My Garden* by Arnold and Anita Lobel (see bibliography for other options)
- several types of honey
- wooden coffee stirrers
- honeycomb

For the flowered paper (optional)
- four 4″ squares of white construction paper
- 4″ squares of newsprint for cutting practice
- crayons

For the teacher and each child to make a flower quilt block
- one May flower blackline, page 151
- five 2″ squares of white or flowered paper (made with materials listed above)
- five 2″ squares of light green construction paper
- one 2″ square of yellow construction paper
- scissors and glue

For the teacher and each child to make a bee
- picture of a bee
- one 2″ x 1½″ oval of white construction paper
- one 2″ square of black construction paper
- about thirty 1½″ squares each of yellow and black tissue paper
- two 1½″ squares of blue tissue paper
- pencils
- black crayons
- scissors and glue

To assemble the quilt
- all the dry flower and bee quilt blocks
- one color cube per child
- one large sheet of yellow bulletin board paper
- glue

Introducing the Quilt

Read and discuss books about bees. Talk about the bee's job of pollinating flowers and making honey. Bring in honey and honeycomb. If possible, have samples of the flowers from which the honey was taken. Pass out sample tastes of the honey on wooden coffee stirrers. Cut the honeycomb into bite-sized pieces for the children to sample.

Find recipes for honey cake, cookies or bread and prepare them with the class. Tell the children they are going to make a a flower and bee quilt in honor of the bee.

Making the Flower Quilt Block

Overview

- ▼ Children make the flowered paper (optional).
- ▼ Introduce the May flower blackline.
- ▼ Children learn how to construct a flower quilt block.
- ▼ Children make their own flower quilt blocks.

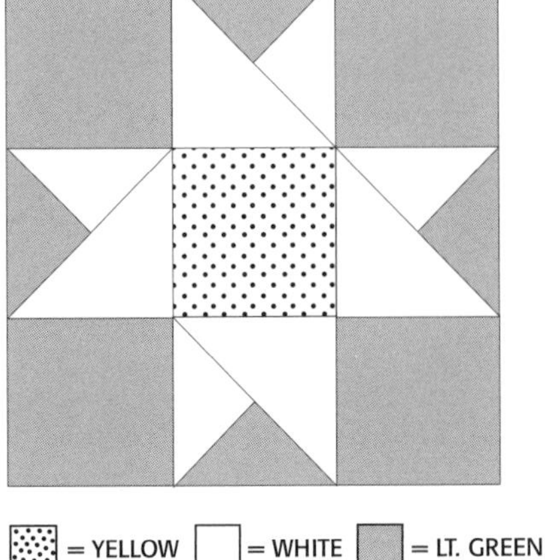

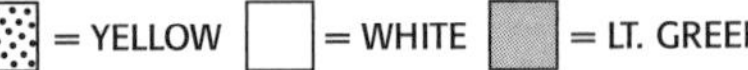

Designing the Flowered Paper (Optional)

Note: This is an optional step. You may choose to use white paper instead.

Show the children a sample white paper square with flowers and leaves drawn on it, and explain that the flower petals on their quilt blocks will be made with flowered paper. Tell them they will use crayons to "sprinkle" the flowers and leaves over their paper to look like they're growing wild in a field. The flowers can be many different colors or all the same color. They may also lightly color the background. Place the 4″ white paper squares and crayons at the tables. Have the children go to their tables to draw the flowers. Cut the flower paper into fourths (into 2″ squares).

Have the 2″ paper squares, and scissors and blacklines on hand.

Gather the children at the rug. Give each a flower blackline. Have volunteers describe what they see.

Tammy: *It looks like a flower.*
Nicholas: *It has squares and triangles. Some of the triangles are small.*
Esse: *I think it will have three colors.*

Explore area as you help the children compute the number of squares of each color needed to cover the quilt block. See Early Experiences in Area, page 12, for this discussion.

Hold up some white (or flowered white) squares and your flower blackline and explain that the squares will be used to cover the petals. Explain that you have only squares, no triangles, with which to cover the petals. Challenge the children to find a way to make triangles from the squares. If they suggest cutting the squares in half diagonally, make sure they understand that each triangle is one-half of a square.

Explore the ideas that a square is made up of two triangles and that each triangle is half of the square. See Triangles and Halves, page 8, for this discussion.

Help them discover that the triangles are too large to cover the smaller white triangles on the blackline. Point out that the smaller triangles are half the size of the larger triangles.

Explore the ideas that one of the triangles is made up of two smaller triangles and that each small triangle is a quarter of the square. See Triangles and Quarters, page 10, for this discussion.

Challenge the children to find a way to cut smaller triangles to cover the small white triangles. You should have extra squares on hand for experimentation. Have the children share their ideas. When they suggest cutting the larger triangles in half, help them understand that four of the smaller triangles make one square.

Ask the children how many squares they will need altogether to cover the white triangles on the blackline. Count out the number of squares suggested and test their predictions.

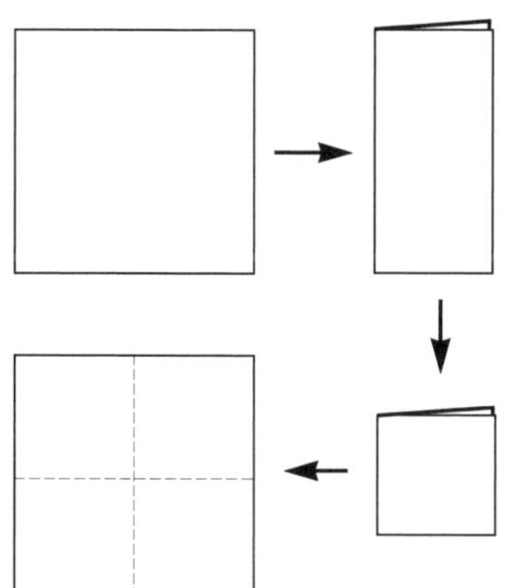

Display some light green paper squares and explain that they will be used to cover the shaded background. Ask the children how to get triangles from the squares. Help them discover that the triangles they get by cutting a square in half are too large to cover the shaded triangles on the blackline, and that these small triangles are half the size of the larger triangles. Remind them that this is the same problem they tackled with the white (or flowered) triangles. Ask the children how to cut smaller triangles to cover the shaded triangles on the blackline, and test their solutions. Then ask how many light green squares they will need altogether to cover the shaded squares and triangles.

Point out that the yellow square will cover the dotted square in the center of the flower.

Place the flowered or plain white paper squares, light green squares, yellow squares and scissors at the tables. Have the children go to their tables to cut and place the squares correctly onto the flower blacklines. If they've been using newsprint for practice, distribute the flowered or plain white paper only once they understand how to cut the triangles. Encourage them to be careful and to check before they cut out the smaller triangles.

DON'T put glue on the tables until everyone has placed his or her pieces correctly.

Then distribute glue to the tables. When the children have finished gluing the squares and triangles in place, have them cut out their quilt blocks carefully around the edges so no white remains.

Step 2

Constructing the Bee

Overview

- ▼ Introduce the tissue paper bee.
- ▼ Children learn how to construct a tissue paper bee with the teacher's help.
- ▼ Children make their own tissue paper bees and glue them on the flower quilt blocks.

Have the tissue paper squares, construction paper squares and ovals, bee picture, pencil, crayons, and scissors on hand.

Gather the children at the rug. Explain that you will show them how to make bees to put on their flower quilt blocks. Show them a white construction paper oval and a picture of a bee. Tell them that their bees will have two yellow stripes and two black stripes. Show them how to divide the oval body of the bee into four sections. Demonstrate labeling the sections Y (yellow), B (black), Y (yellow), B (black).

Work with a volunteer to cut two antennae from the 2″ square of black construction paper. Show how to paste them at one end of the oval.

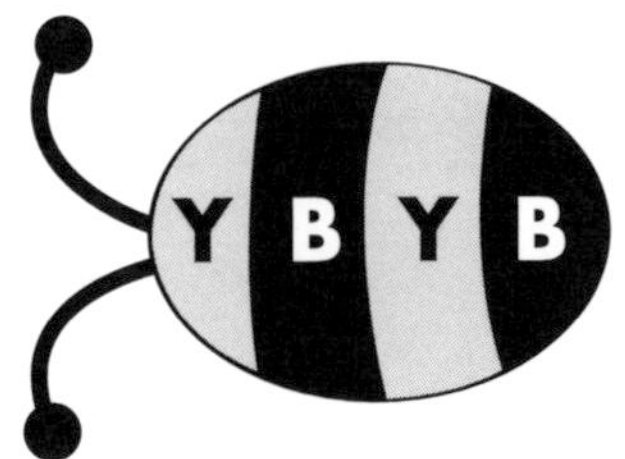

Show the children the tissue paper squares. Explain that the yellow and black squares are for the body and the blue squares are for the wings. Demonstrate gluing the yellow and black tissue paper to the white oval:

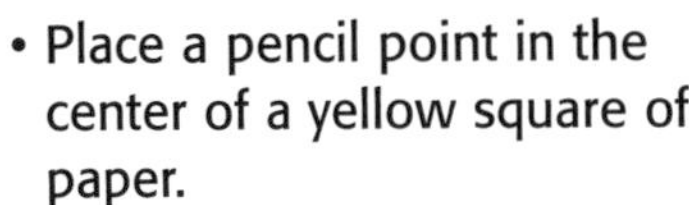

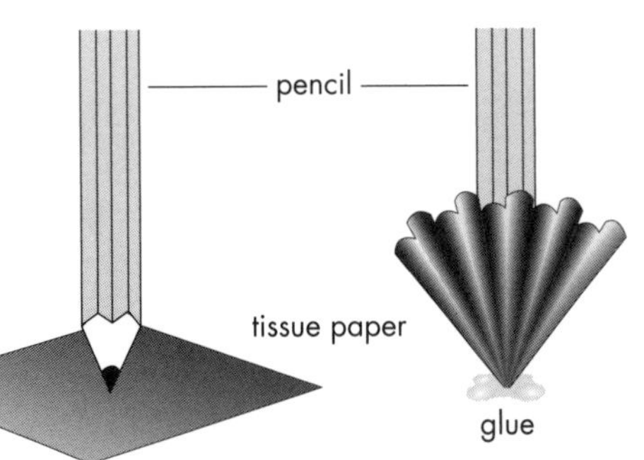

- Place a pencil point in the center of a yellow square of paper.
- Crease the sides of the square up and around the pencil.
- With the pencil inside the paper, dip the paper in the glue and stick it to the body of the bee.
- Tightly apply all the squares to the body and make it look fluffy.

Have volunteers help you apply tissue paper until the bee's body is covered with fluffy yellow and black stripes.

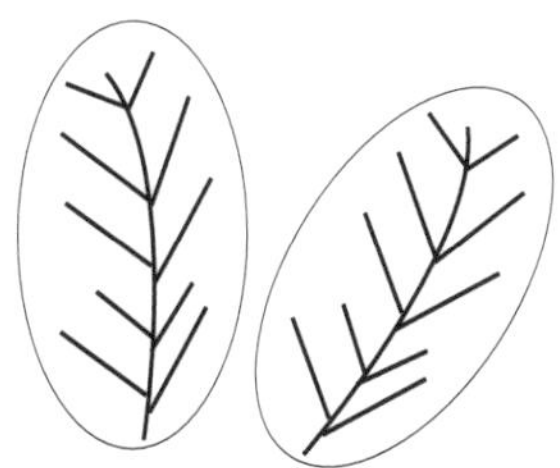

Draw and cut out two ovals from the blue squares. Cut them from corner to corner to get the largest possible ovals. Draw some veins with crayon to make the ovals look like wings.

Wrap one end of the oval around the end of a pencil, dip it in glue and affix it near the center of the bee's body. Do the same with the second wing.

Place bee materials at the tables. Have the children go to their tables to make their own bees. Set the bees aside to dry. Distribute the flower quilt blocks and have the children glue the dried bees diagonally in the center of the flowers.

Assembling the Quilt

See Computing the Size of the Quilt, page 17, for a discussion of shape and dimensions.

Gather the children at the rug. Place the bulletin board paper and the finished quilt blocks in the center of the rug. Tell them the class will decide on a good size and shape for the quilt together.

Depending on the number of children in your room, you will need to decide how long to make each row of the quilt. Figure it so you arrive at a good size rectangle or square. For example, if you have twenty blocks, your rectangle can be 5 x 4, with no extra blocks. For twenty-six blocks, your rectangle can be 6 x 4, with two extra blocks.

Practice pattern skills while laying out each row of the quilt. See Predicting Patterns, page 20, for this discussion.

As you start to place the blocks on the bulletin board paper, you might suggest alternating the direction the bees are facing. While assembling the quilt, children can predict the pattern.

See Making Quilt Block Pillows, page 20, for how to turn leftover quilt blocks into a mini art project.

If you have leftover blocks, you can make them into pillows.

Glue the finished quilt on the bulletin board paper, leaving a border.

Searching for Patterns and Designs

See Hidden Patterns and Designs, page 22, for a complete discussion of exploring patterns in finished quilts.

Hang the finished quilt on the wall for all to admire. Encourage the children to find designs and patterns hidden in the quilt. You may choose to record their comments on paper idea bubbles and attach them to the quilt.

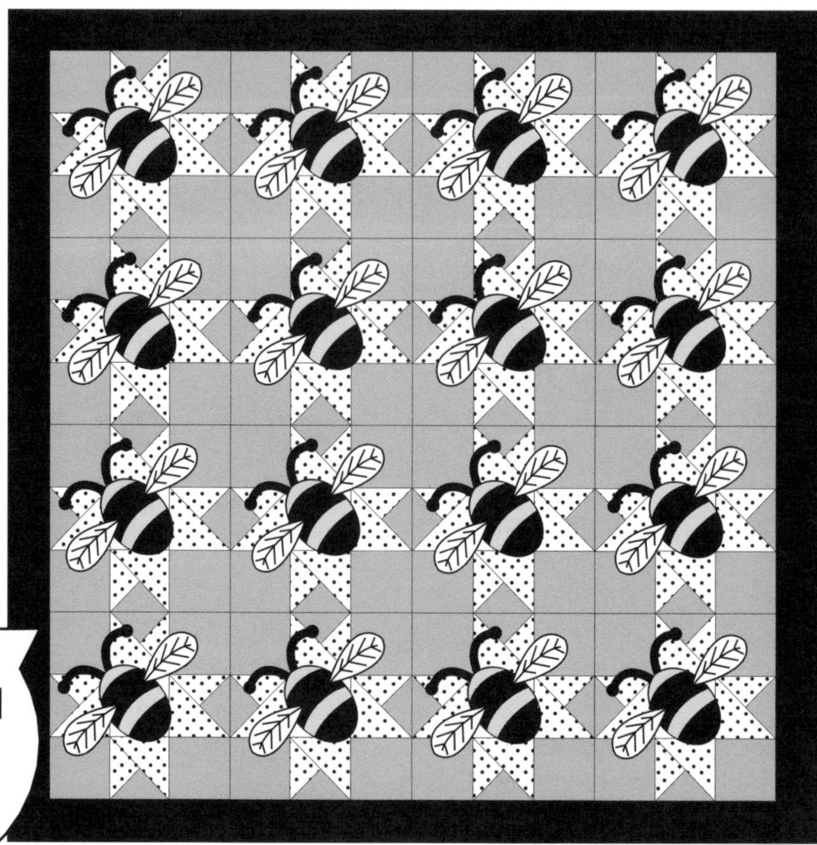

It goes flower, diamond, flower, diamond down and across.
Four small squares make a big blue square.
There's a blue diamond in between every flower.

May Flower

Note: This quilt is assembled from four-block squares. You will need a number of quilt blocks that is divisible by eight (16, 24, 32, etc.). You might need to make extra quilt blocks.

Flag Quilt

Lesson Synopsis

Materials Needed

Use the optional discussion topics and activities to introduce the flag quilt.

For the introduction (optional)
- *Sewing Quilts* by Ann Turner
- your own quilt(s) brought from home

The teacher and the class meet at the rug. The teacher introduces the flag quilt block that will form the quilt. The children explore the ideas of area and one-half as they learn how to construct the block with the teacher's help. Then they go to the tables to make their own flag quilt blocks.

For the teacher and each child to make a flag quilt block
- one flag blackline, page 157
- six 1½" squares of bright red construction paper
- six 1½" squares of white construction paper
- four 1½" squares of dark blue construction paper
- white tempera paint
- scissors and glue

When the glued blocks have dried, the children work in small groups to find patterns in a four-block quilt square. They gather at the rug, share their patterns, and select their favorite. The quilt is assembled from multiples of the selected square and glued on bulletin board paper.

To assemble the quilt
- all the dry flag quilt blocks
- one large sheet of bright blue bulletin board paper
- one color cube per child
- glue

The quilt is displayed on the wall, and the children discuss patterns they see in it.

Introducing the Quilt

If this is your last quilt of the school year, help children recall all the quilts they have made. Ask them what they have learned about making something for everyone to share. Talk about how quilts are made of memories and how making a quilt can be a bonding experience. Everyone makes a small part, and when all the parts are assembled into a whole, something beautiful results that surprises us all.

If you have a special quilt of your own, share it with your students. Tell them how you acquired it and why you love it.

Read and discuss *Sewing Quilts* by Anne Turner. Talk about the softly illustrated scenes and the themes of family closeness and safety. Discuss how the children in the story feel about making and having quilts.

Tell the children they are going to make Mollie's flag quilt to celebrate the Fourth of July.

Making the Flag Quilt Block

Overview

- ▼ Introduce the flag blackline.
- ▼ Children learn how to construct a flag quilt block.
- ▼ Children make their own flag quilt blocks.

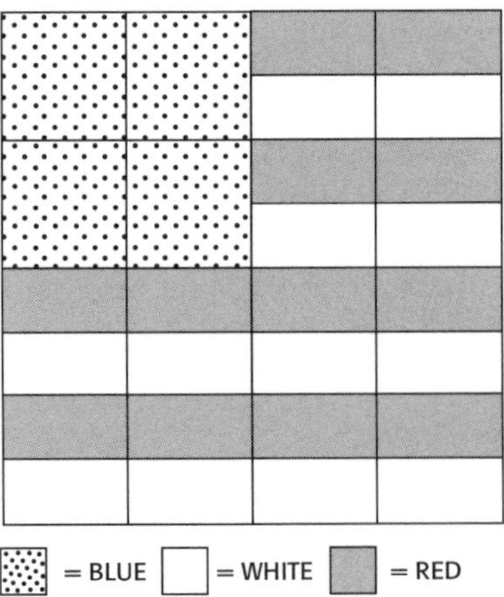

Have the 1½″ paper squares, scissors and blacklines on hand.

Gather the children at the rug. Give each a flag blackline. Have volunteers describe what they see.

Katherine: *It looks like a flag.*
Richard: *But there are no stars on it.*
Alipate: *There are squares and stripes, no triangles.*

Explore the ideas that a square is made up of two rectangles and that each rectangle is half of the square. See Rectangles and Halves, page 10, for this discussion.

Explore area as you help the children compute the number of squares of each color needed to cover the quilt block. See Early Experiences in Area, page 12, for this discussion.

Show the children that you have only red and white squares, no rectangles, with which to cover the stripes on the flag. Challenge the children to find a way to make rectangles from the squares. You should have extra squares on hand for experimentation. Have the children share their ideas.

Have the children figure out the number of red and white squares needed to cover the stripes on the flag. Count out the numbers of squares suggested and test their predictions.

Ask the children to figure out how many blue squares are needed to cover the dotted squares on the blackline and test their predictions.

DON'T put glue on the tables until you are sure children have placed their pieces correctly.

Place the paper squares (one color at a time) and scissors at the tables. Have the children go to their tables to cut and place the squares correctly onto the flag blacklines. Once they have placed the first color, put out the second color, and so on.

Then distribute glue to the tables. When the children have finished gluing all the squares and rectangles in place, have them cut out their quilt blocks carefully around the edges so no white remains.

Tell children they will add stars to their flags. Place shallow containers of white tempera paint at each table. Demonstrate how to dip one finger in white tempera and put four white dots in each blue square, representing stars.

Have children add stars to their flags. Put the blocks aside to dry.

Assembling the Quilt

Help children discover patterns in the four-block quilt squares. See Slides and Rotations, page 14, for this discussion.

Divide the children into groups of four and give each group four flag quilt blocks. Show the children how to place the four blocks together to make a four-block quilt square. Demonstrate that new designs are created by sliding or rotating the blocks in different ways.

Encourage groups to experiment rotating the blocks to find a variety of designs. Allow time for children to walk around and see other groups' designs.

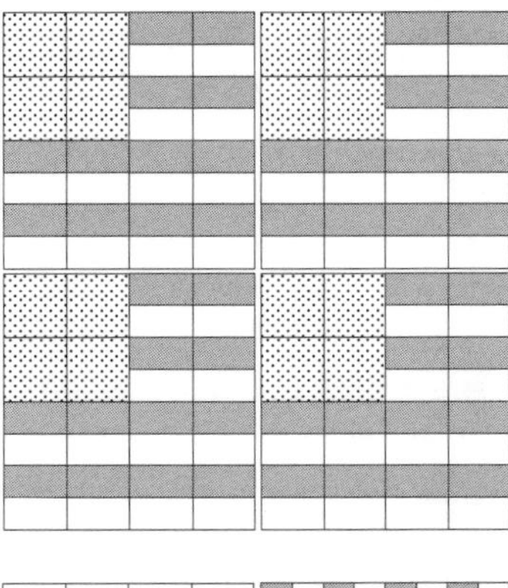

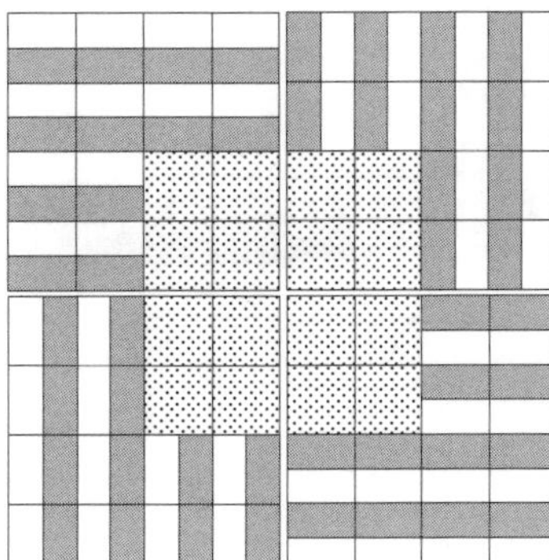

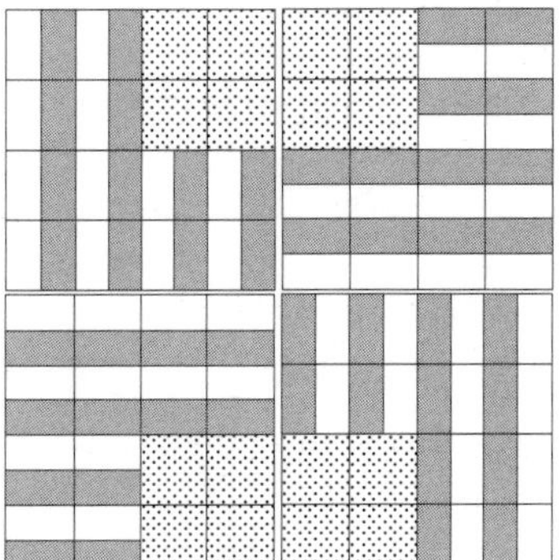

Ask each group to arrange its favorite four-block design on the rug. Give each child a color cube. Explain that each person may cast one vote for his or her favorite design by placing a color cube on that design. Then have each group build the selected quilt square from its four blocks.

See Making Quilt Block Pillows, page 20, for how to turn leftover quilt blocks into a mini art project.

If you have leftover blocks, you can make them into pillows.

Arrange all the four-block quilt squares on the bulletin board paper to make the finished design. Glue them on the bulletin board paper, leaving a border.

Searching for Patterns and Designs

See Hidden Patterns and Designs, page 22, for a complete discussion of exploring patterns in finished quilts.

Hang the quilt on the wall for all to admire. Encourage the children to find designs and patterns hidden in the quilt. You may choose to record their comments on paper idea bubbles and attach them to the quilt.

There are four big blue squares in the middle of the quilt.

The stripes go sideways down, sideways up around the blue squares.

The stripes go red, white, red, white.

Flag

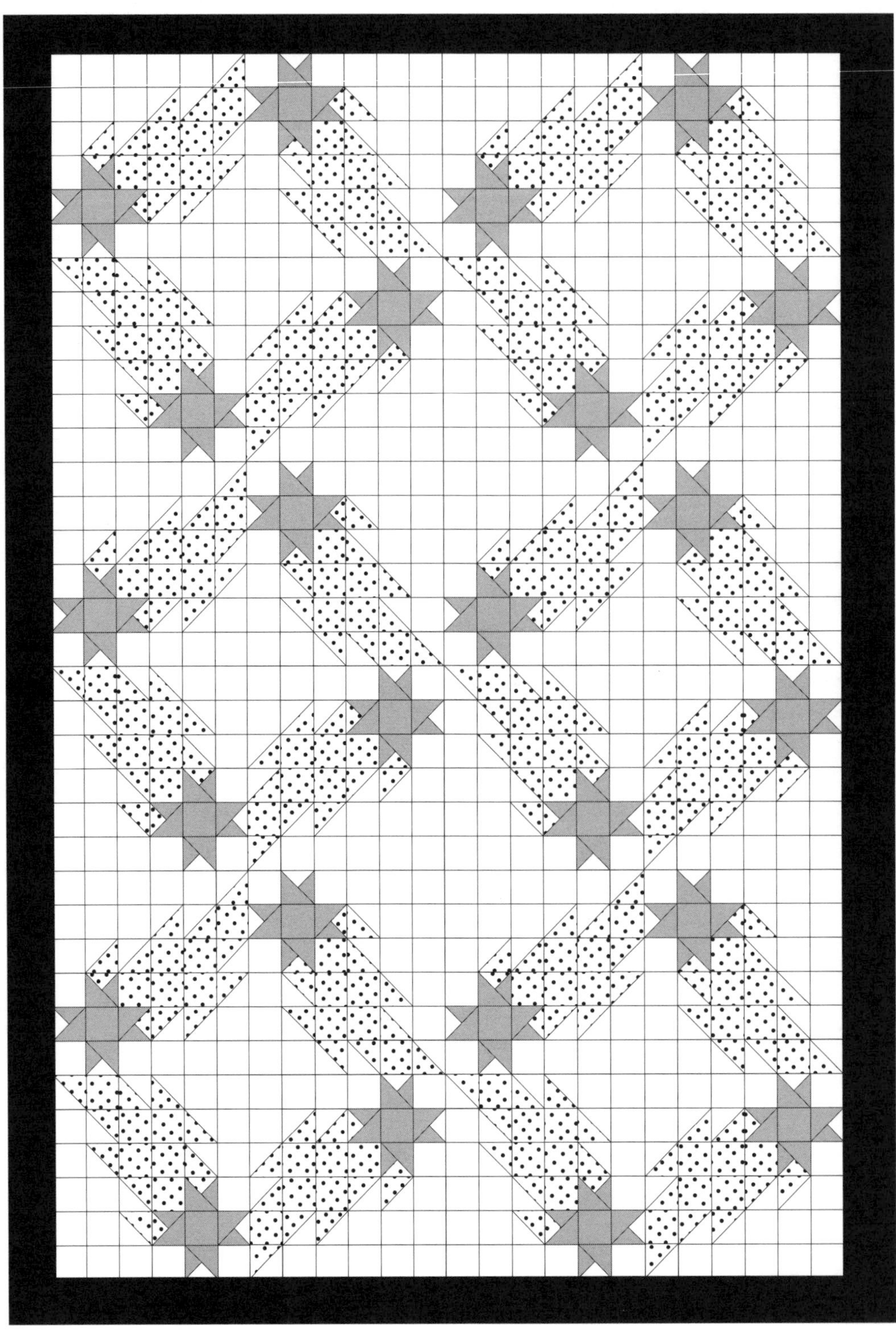

Note: This quilt is assembled from four-block squares. You will need a number of quilt blocks that is divisible by eight (16, 24, 32, etc.). You might need to make extra quilt blocks.

Roman Candle Quilt

Lesson Synopsis

Use the optional discussion topics and activities to introduce the Roman candle quilt.

The teacher and the class meet at the rug. The teacher introduces the Roman candle quilt block that will form the quilt. The children explore the ideas of area, one-half and one-quarter as they learn how to construct the block with the teacher's help. Then they go to the tables to make their own Roman candle quilt blocks.

When the glued blocks have dried, the children work in small groups to find patterns in a four-block quilt square. They gather at the rug, share their patterns, and select their favorite. The quilt is assembled from multiples of the selected square and glued on bulletin board paper.

The quilt is displayed on the wall, and the children discuss patterns they see in it.

Materials Needed

For the introduction (optional)
- *Sewing Quilts* by Ann Turner
- your own quilt(s) brought from home

For the teacher and each child to make a Roman candle quilt block
- one Roman candle blackline, page 163
- four 1″ squares of red metallic wrapping paper
- eleven 1″ squares of gold metallic wrapping paper
- twenty-one 1″ squares of dark blue construction paper
- scissors and glue

To assemble the quilt
- all the Roman candle quilt blocks
- one color cube per child
- one large sheet of black or gold metallic bulletin board paper
- glue

Introducing the Quilt

If this is your last quilt of the school year, help children recall all the quilts they have made. Ask them what they have learned about making something for everyone to share. Talk about how quilts are made of memories and how making a quilt can be a bonding experience. Everyone makes a small part, and when all the parts are assembled into a whole, something beautiful results that surprises us all.

If you have a special quilt of your own, share it with your students. Tell them how you acquired it and why you love it.

Read and discuss *Sewing Quilts* by Anne Turner. Talk about the softly illustrated scenes and the themes of family closeness and safety. Discuss how the children in the story feel about making and having quilts.

Tell the children they are going to make a Roman candle quilt to celebrate the Fourth of July.

Making the Roman Candle Quilt Block

Overview

- ▼ Introduce the Roman candle blackline.
- ▼ Children learn how to construct a Roman candle quilt block.
- ▼ Children make their own Roman candle quilt blocks.

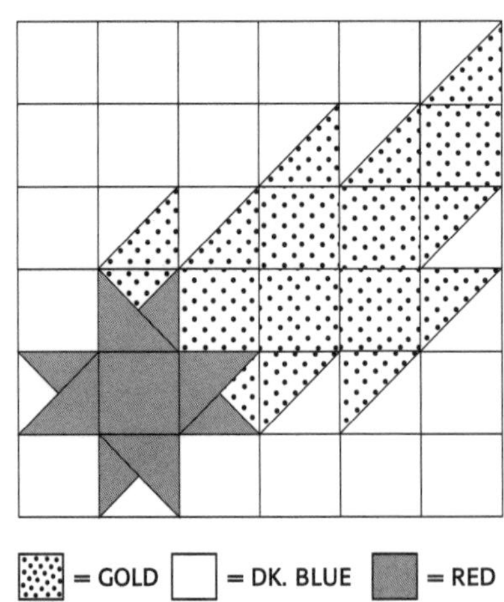

Have the 1″ paper squares, scissors and blacklines on hand.

Gather the children at the rug. Give each a Roman candle blackline. Have volunteers describe what they see.

Show the children the colored squares. Ask them where they think the different colors should be placed on the Roman candle blackline.

Michael: *In the story the rocket was red, so I think the star should be red. The gray part should be red.*
Teacher: *What about the gold squares?*
Nicholas: *They will make the fire trail after the star, the dotted part.*
Teacher: *And the blue squares?*
Evelesia: *They make the sky all around it.*

Explore the ideas that a square is made up of two triangles and that each triangle is half of the square. See Triangles and Halves, page 8, for this discussion.

Show the children a red metallic paper square. Explain that you have only squares, no triangles, with which to cover the star. Challenge them to find a way to make triangles from the square.

Help the children discover that the triangles are too large to cover the shaded triangles on the blackline. Point out that the smaller triangles are half the size of the larger triangles.

Explore the ideas that one of the triangles is made up of two smaller triangles and that each small triangle is a quarter of the square. See Triangles and Quarters, page 10, for this discussion.

Challenge the children to find a way to cut smaller triangles to cover the shaded triangles on the blackline. You might want to have extra squares on hand for experimentation. Have the children share their ideas. When they suggest cutting the larger triangles in half, help them understand that four of the smaller triangles make one square.

Explore area as you help the children compute the number of squares of each color needed to cover the quilt block. See Early Experiences in Area, page 12, for this discussion.

Ask the children to figure out how many red squares they will need to cover the star. Count out the number of squares suggested and test their predictions.

Challenge the children to figure out how many gold squares they will need to cover the trail of light from the star. Make sure they see that they will need two small triangles.

Repeat the procedure to determine how many blue squares they will need to cover the background. Once again, point out they will need two small triangles.

DON'T put glue on the tables until everyone has placed his or her pieces correctly.

Place the paper squares (one color at a time) and scissors at the tables. Have the children go to the tables to cut and place the squares correctly onto the Roman candle blacklines. Once they have placed the first color, put out the second color, and so on.

Then distribute glue to the tables. When the children have finished gluing all the squares and triangles in place, have them cut out their quilt blocks carefully around the edges so no white remains. Put the blocks aside to dry.

Assembling the Quilt

Group the children in fours and give each group four Roman candle quilt blocks. Show the children how to place the four blocks together to make a four-block quilt square. Demonstrate that new designs are created by sliding or rotating the blocks in different ways.

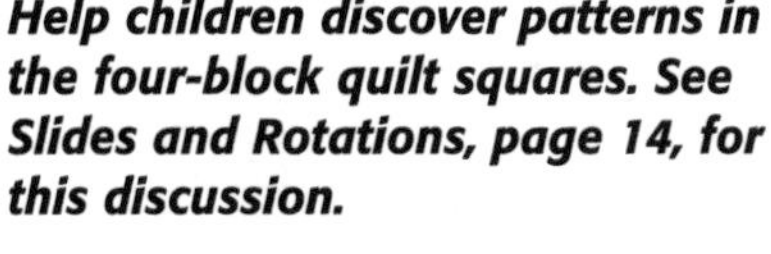

Help children discover patterns in the four-block quilt squares. See Slides and Rotations, page 14, for this discussion.

Encourage groups to experiment rotating the blocks to find a variety of designs. Allow time for children to walk around and see other groups' designs.

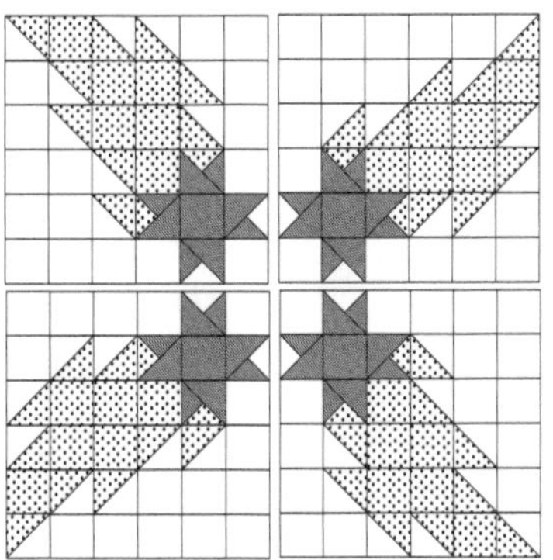

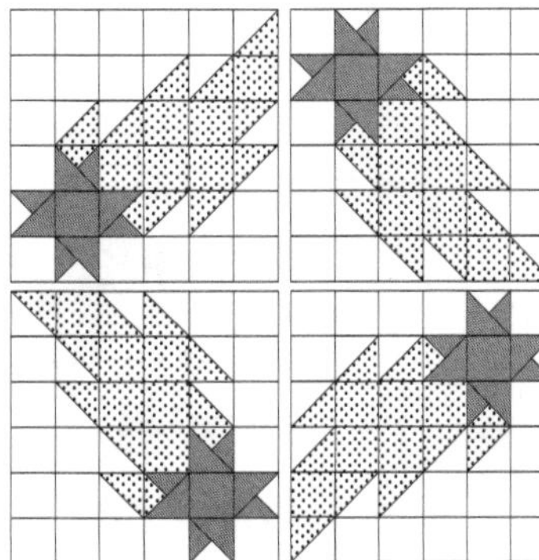

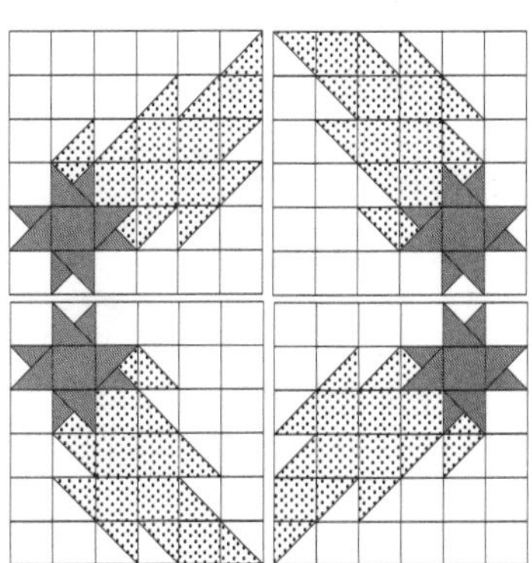

Ask each group to arrange its favorite four-block design on the rug. Give each child a color cube. Explain that each person may cast one vote for his or her favorite design by placing a color cube on that design. Then have each group build the selected quilt square from its four blocks.

See Making Quilt Block Pillows, page 20, for how to turn leftover quilt blocks into a mini art project.

If you have leftover blocks, you can make them into pillows.

Arrange all the quilt squares on the bulletin board paper to make the finished design. Glue them on the bulletin board paper, leaving a border.

Searching for Patterns and Designs

See Hidden Patterns and Designs, page 22, for a complete discussion of exploring patterns in finished quilts.

Hang the quilt on the wall for all to admire. Encourage the children to find designs and patterns hidden in the quilt. You may choose to record their comments on paper idea bubbles and attach them to the quilt.

A Roman candle makes a jaggedy diamond.

Four stars come together to make a fence around a big blue square.

Around each blue square it goes star, diamond, star, diamond.

Roman Candle

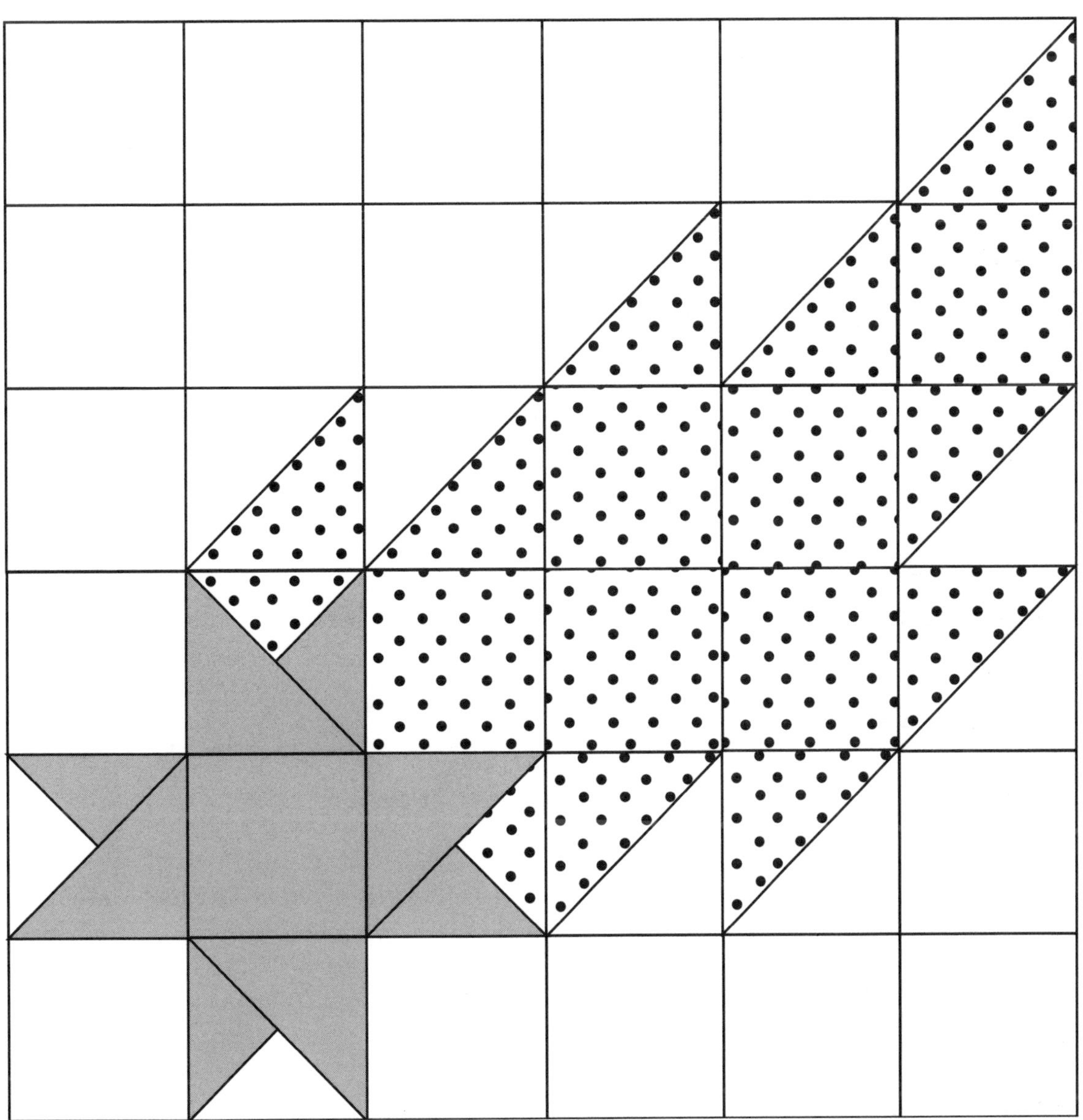

Bibliography

Confer, Chris. *Math By All Means: Geometry, Grades 1-2.* Sausalito, CA: Math Solutions Publications, 1994.

Ehlert, Lois. *Fish Eyes: A Book You Can Count On*. New York: Harcourt Brace, 1992. [Rainbow Fish Quilt]

Ehlert, Lois. *Snowballs*. San Diego: Harcourt Brace, 1995. [Snowman Quilt]

Flournoy, Valerie. *The Patchwork Quilt.* New York: Penguin, 1985. [Valentine Heart Quilt]

Gibbons, Gail. *The Honey Makers.* New York: William Morrow, 1997. [Flower and Bee Quilt]

Gibbons, Gail. *St. Patrick's Day.* New York: Holiday House, 1985. [Shamrock Quilt]

Ginsburg, Mirra. *Good Morning Chick!* New York: Scholastic, 1980. [Chick Quilt]

Hoffman, James. *The Christmas Wreath.* Grand Haven, MI: School Zone Publishing Co., 1993. [Polar Bear Quilt]

Holub, Joan. *Red Yellow Green . . . What do Signs Mean?* New York: Scholastic, 1998. [Traffic Light and Stop Sign Quilts]

Hopkinson, Deborah. *Sweet Clara and the Freedom Quilt.* Alfred A. Knopf, Inc., New York, 1993. [River and Trees Quilt]

Hutchins, Pat. *The Wind Blew.* New York: Simon & Schuster, 1993. [Pinwheel Quilt]

Lobel, Arnold. *The Rose in My Garden.* New York: William Morrow, 1993. [Flower and Bee Quilt]

Loewen, Nancy. *Traffic Safety: Safety Sense Series.* Chanhassen, MN: Child's World, 1996. [Traffic Light and Stop Sign Quilts]

MacMillan, Dianne. *Presidents Day.* Springfield, NJ: Enslow Publishers, Inc., 1997. [Presidents' Quilt]

Micucci, Charles. *The Life and Times of the Honeybee.* Boston: Houghton Mifflin, 1997.
[Flower and Bee Quilt]

Orie, Sandra De Coteau. *Did You Hear Wind Sing Your Name? An Oneida Song of Spring.* New York: Walker & Co., 1995.
[Pinwheel Quilt]

Paul, Ann Whitford. *The Seasons Sewn*. San Diego: Harcourt Brace, 1996.
[Pine Tree Quilt]

Scheer, Julian. *Rain Makes Applesauce.* New York: Holiday House, 1985.
[Flower and Raindrop Quilt]

Smucker, Barbara. *Selina and The Bear Paw Quilt.* New York: Crown Publishers, Inc., 1995.
[Polar Bear Quilt]

Turner, Ann. *Sewing Quilts*. New York: Macmillan Publishing, 1994.
[Flag and Roman Candle Quilts]

Wahl, Jan. *"I Remember," Cried Grandma Pinky.* Mahwah, NJ: BridgeWater Books, 1997.
[Polar Bear Quilt]

Waters, Kate. *Tapenum's Day: A Wampanoag Indian Boy in Pilgrim Times.* New York: Scholastic, 1996.
[Native American Quilt]

Waters, Kate. *Sarah Morton's Day. A Day in the Life of a Pilgrim Girl*. New York: Scholastic, 1989.
[Pilgrim Quilt]

Waters, Kate. *Samuel Eaton's Day. A Day in the Life of a Pilgrim Boy*. New York: Scholastic, 1993.
[Pilgrim Quilt]

Webster, Vera. *Weather Experiments.* Danbury, CT: Children's Press, 1982.
[Pinwheel Quilt]

Zagwÿn, Deborah Turney. *The Pumpkin Blanket*. Berkeley, CA: Celestial Arts, 1990.
[Jack-O'-Lantern and Pumpkin Quilts]